TALES OF THE BORDERS

TALES OF THE BORDERS

MICHAEL BRANDER

MAINSTREAM
PUBLISHING

First published in 1991 by
MAINSTREAM PUBLISHING COMPANY
(EDINBURGH) LTD
7 Albany Street
Edinburgh EH1 3UG

Typeset in 11 on 12pt Baskerville by
Blackpool Typesetters Ltd., Blackpool
Printed and bound in Great Britain by Billings & Sons, Worcester

For my brother

Francis Everett Brander

CONTENTS

INTRODUCTION

IN 1834 John Mackay Wilson at the age of twenty-eight published the first of his *Tales of the Borders* in the *Berwick Advertiser*. He died within a year of the first weekly copy, but had the satisfaction of seeing the circulation rise from 2,000 to 16,000—a phenomenal figure in those days. The *Tales* were then published in book form in 1840, edited by Alexander Leighton, and went into numerous editions, the last of which was published in the mid-1930s. They sold remarkably well all round the world.

When I was asked to write this book it seemed to me that I could not do better than produce a slightly edited selection of some of the better *Tales*. It also seemed desirable to give those readers with no knowledge of the Borders, or of Scotland, some idea of the historical background as well as pointing their feet in the right direction if they should decide to visit the area. It is for this reason that I have placed the *Tales* in more or less chronological order historically and have added brief notes on the area in which the events took place. For those who have read and enjoyed the *Tales* in the original and for those who know the Borders well, I must apologise if it seems that at times I have bowdlerised the originals, or changed them out of all recogition by removing too much of the original Scots vernacular. I have tried, however, to retain the essential character and feel of the *Tales* themselves, while

9

at the same time making them readily intelligible, I trust, to any reader, even those whose first language is not necessarily English.

After the Scots defeated the Norwegians under King Hakon at the battle of Largs, in 1263, they turned away from Scandinavian influence towards Europe. Before the end of the century, in 1295, the Scots had already formed their first alliance with France against the English. This was renewed periodically for nearly 300 years until the Treaty of Leith, in 1560, saw the triumph of the Reformation in Scotland aided by the English and then "The Auld Alliance" passed gradually into history.

The initial reason for it was the largely unprovoked aggression of the English under Edward I, "the Hammer of the Scots". In the face of continuous attacks, when not only the Border countryside was ravaged but the whole of Scotland invaded, a united Scottish Nation was forged on the anvil of hatred amid the fierce heat of desperation.

From Scotland's first Treaty of Alliance with France in 1295 until Bruce defeated them at Bannockburn in 1314 the English forces invaded and pillaged the length and breadth of Scotland. It was not until 1328, the year prior to Bruce's death, that the English were finally forced to recognise Scotland as an independent nation. Even then, for more than 200 years, until as late as 1549, the English still periodically invaded Scotland and a legacy of bitterness was left which survived for nearly four centuries until the Union of the Parliaments in 1707. Even today the smouldering embers are capable of being fanned into life. Nowhere was this more apparent than in the Borders which bore the brunt of successive raids and invasions from either side.

The spirit of lawlessness, which is to be found in any area where fighting is the normal way of life and might is right, prevailed on both sides of the Borders of Scotland and England right up to the Union of the Crowns in 1603, despite successive efforts by the rulers of both Scotland and England to put a stop to it. The institution on each side of the Border of a system of Wardens who met periodically in times of peace and attempted to legislate on various disputes was always open to abuse by either side. The loyalties and treachery, the blood-ties and double dealing as well as the sheer savagery of many of those who fought on either side made life a misery for the poor and a political tightrope for the remainder. Blood feuds and hereditary enmities were commonplace, their origins often forgotten by the participants. Belief in witchcraft and religious persecution added to the complications of life in the period covered by these *Tales*.

As only one example of a survival of those days, there is a game still played annually in Jedburgh between the two ends of the town, one end of which is known as the "Uppies" and the other as the "Doonies". The shops are all closely shuttered and the entire town closes for the period of the game on the day in question. Several balls are released in the centre of the town and the object is to get them to the goal at the opposite end of the town by any means. Once there, each ball is nicked with a knife. This traditional game stems from a battle when the town was recaptured, after which the "balls" used were Englishmen's heads.

In case anyone should think this an exaggeration let them read the account by a M. de Beague, a French officer sent to the aid of the Scots in 1549, who wrote of their treatment of an English prisoner as follows:

> They tied his hands and feet and head together and placed him thus trussed in the middle of an open space and ran upon him with their lances, armed as they were and on horseback . . . until he was dead and his body hacked in a thousand pieces, which they divided among them and carried away on the iron points of their spears. I cannot greatly praise the Scots for this practice, but the truth is the English tyrannised over the Borders in a most barbarous manner and I think it was fair to repay them, as the saying goes, in their own coin.

Like the period of North American history when the West was being settled, when cowboys and Indians and cattle

11

rustlers, bank robbers and law men fought gun battles with each other, this is a period which has been romanticised by many writers. It should be appreciated that as with the Wild West much of the life was dirty, unpleasant, unhygienic and vicious. Moral standards were low to non-existent and only the tough survived. Yet there was also, in the Borders at least, laughter and loyalty, courage and bravery of a high degree, and many fine characteristics were implanted in the people which have survived to the present day.

The following tales date from the thirteenth to the seventeenth centuries and are presented in chronological sequence. As far as possible the location of each is also indicated.

THE DOOM OF SOULIS

The first tale concerns the Earl of Soulis, who appears to have been a sadistic and unpleasant tyrant, a cross between the Marquis de Sade and Count Dracula. He was famed as a wizard and for practising the Black Arts, but in those days the reputation of a wizard was not difficult to acquire. For instance, Thomas Learmont of Earlston, or Thomas of Ercildoune, or Thomas the Rhymer, as he is variously known was famed as a soothsayer in the Borders at much the same period, forecasting King Alexander III's death in 1285 and Bruce's victories over the English. It was said that he had spent several years with the Queen of Elfland in his youth when he was granted the gift of prophecy. Like many another scholar of those days, however, the probability is that he had spent several years studying at foreign universities, which could very well have given rise to such a tale. Another with a similar reputation of much the same period was Hugo de Gifford of East Lothian, so that the Earl of Soulis was by no means exceptional even if the tale of his death owes more to legend than fact.

> They rolled him up in a sheet of lead –
> A sheet of lead for a funeral pall;
> They plunged him in the cauldron red,
> And melted him – lead, bones and all.
>
> Leyden

13

HERMITAGE CASTLE stands solitary and brooding in a desolate, windswept glen amongst the bare Border hills, far to the south of Hawick. It is a square forbidding ruin, all that remains of the widely feared wizard the Earl of Soulis's erstwhile home. In the thirteenth century it must have seemed an isolated, menacing and almost impregnable stronghold. It is easy enough for the most unimaginative to understand the dread in which the owner once was held, for there is still an aura of something not exactly wholesome about that solid pile. At the end of the thirteenth century it was the home of a man who with good reason was credited with supernatural powers by all who knew him.

Lord Soulis by all accounts was not a man to be trifled with by anyone. His neighbours both feared and loathed him. His retainers dared not cross him and went in mortal terror of his every word. He was not only a tyrant who actively enjoyed inflicting pain on others, but he was also renowned as a sorcerer who had sold his soul to the devil. Having made a pact with the devil it was said he kept his familiar evil spirit locked in an iron-bound chest in a dungeon in the depths beneath his castle where unmentionable practices were carried out at dead of night.

Although a perpetual outcry was raised against him and his evil deeds from the banks of the Tweed, Teviot and the Jed as far as the Lothians, he escaped retribution, for it was said that his life was protected by an evil charm and no mortal weapons were able to prevail against him. Apart from being a man of immense size and outstandingly powerful he also claimed to have royal blood in his veins. He even claimed that his right to the crown of Scotland was greater than that of Bruce.

He had, however, at this time, one overpowering wish, even greater than his desire for the crown of Scotland, which was to marry an exceedingly rich and beautiful maiden, named Marion, who lived nearby in the Border country. She, however, was pledged to marry Sir Walter Scott, the young heir of Branxholm, who was one of the stoutest and boldest young men in the whole of the Borders

14

countryside. Such a detail did not perturb Soulis, who was a man prepared to go to any lengths, however vile they might be, to gain his ends.

In this instance, legend has it, he first went down to the deepest dungeon of his castle, where only he was ever allowed and where no one else dared to go. In one mailed fist he carried a pure black cat held firmly by the scruff of its neck despite its piteous mewing and struggles. Behind him willy-nilly came a black dog which was dragged along howling dismally on the end of a chain. In front of him he drove a fine young black bull calf that had only lived on its mother's milk and had never eaten grass. Once inside the gloomy vaulted dungeon, with the iron-studded door closed behind him and the large key still in the lock, he raised his voice and cried:

"Spirit of Darkness, I come."

He then placed the lamp he carried with him on the ground in the middle of the dungeon floor beside the large iron-bound chest which stood there. Seizing a pick axe and shovel which lay in readiness he then dug a pit and shovelled the earth aside in a heap. Gathering up the cat, which had retreated to the door and was endeavouring to scratch a way out, he threw it into the hole and before it could spring out had shovelled the pile of earth on top of it and buried it alive. As the wretched animal mewed frantically beneath the loose earth he exclaimed again loudly:

"Spirit of Darkness. Come!"

He then leaped on the grave of the slowly dying cat and seized the dog by the scruff of the neck. He hurled it violently against the wall of the dungeon, towards the left hand corner, where it lay howling loudly and piteously with its back broken. Then he plunged a knife into the throat of the young bull. Its plaintive bellowing mingled with the howls of the dying dog and the mews of the suffocating cat. In the semi-darkness and flickering shadows of the vault he held his hands under the bull calf's throat and as the blood gushed forth he stalked round the dungeon, sprinkling it in a circle and crying out loudly:

15

"Spirit of Darkness. Hear me!"

Once more he feverishly dug a pit, on the other side of the iron-bound chest, and seizing the dying bull calf and the dog with its broken spine, he threw them both feet uppermost into the grave and covered them with earth. Not surprisingly the sweat now stood out on his brow in great beads and he was panting with the effort, but he summoned the strength to cry out loudly once again:

"Come, Spirit of Darkness. Come!"

Then he reached for a horseshoe which had lain in the dungeon for years and was known in his family as *the spirit's shoe* and this he nailed obliquely against the inner side of the door. As he gave a last blow to the nail holding it, he cried yet once more:

"Spirit of Darkness. I obey you. Now come to me!"

Then he took his stance in the centre of the vault between the two graves with the slowly suffocating animals inside them and nine times he scattered around him a handful of salt and ashes, each time crying aloud:

"Spirit! Arise! I conjure you to come to me."

He then struck his mailed fist nine times on the lid of the iron-bound chest which stood beside him in the centre of the dungeon. At each blow he cried again:

"Arise, Spirit of Darkness. Arise!"

When he had cried out twenty-seven times the lid of the chest began slowly to rise of its own volition. A ghastly smell as of some newly opened grave which contained the long dead corpses of the victims of some fearful plague filled the room. Then gradually an awesome figure which resembled nothing in any earthly shape or form, rose from the depths of the chest. When the lid of the chest had fully opened a hollow voice which seemed to echo round the chamber in an eerie fashion enquired:

"What is it you want, Soulis?"

"Power, Spirit, power!" he cried. "That I may have all that my eyes desire and that every weapon formed by man shall fall powerless on my body, with no more avail than the waning light of the dying moon."

16

"Thy wish is granted, mortal!" groaned the fiendish spectre. "Tomorrow eve young Branxholm's bride will sit within your walls and his sword will rebound bent from your body, as though it had been smashed against a rock. Farewell! Invoke me not again for seven years, nor open the door of the vault, but then knock three times on the chest and I shall answer you. Away with you now! Follow your courses of sin and prosper. *But beware of a coming wood!*"

With a sudden startling shriek the spirit fiend disappeared and with a loud clang the lid of the ancient iron-bound chest fell firmly shut once more. From underneath the floor of the vault there came a loud and prolonged sound like the rumbling of thunder inside the rock. Soulis seized the lamp and leaving the still-dying animals groaning in their last death throes he locked the iron-studded door of the vault behind him and placed the huge key in his belt.

Next morning Soulis rode out with twenty of his chosen men behind him and by the side of the Teviot water he saw the object of his affections, the fair Marion, affianced bride of young Walter Scott, the heir of Branxholm. She was out riding with her maidens-in-waiting and a few huntsmen in pursuit of the red deer.

"By the power of darkness, Spirit," cried Soulis with pleasure. "You did not lie to me after all. Tonight young Branxholm's bride will indeed sit within my walls."

He was riding a high-mettled black stallion as fleet of foot as any in the whole of the Border country and now he clapped his spurs roughly into its flanks, setting it forward at its fastest gallop. Although Marion and her attendants gave up the hunt and turned to fly as soon as they saw him, none of them stood a chance against Soulis. It was as if his familiar had added wings to his horse's speed. In a few moments he was alongside Marion's horse and, throwing out a powerful metal-clad arm, lifted her effortlessly from the saddle.

She screamed, scratched and struggled with all the spirit which was natural to her, but her efforts were as useless as those of a fly firmly in the grasp of a spider's web. His powerful embrace was such that the breath was knocked out of her and she could barely move while he held her firmly in the saddle before him. With a lash of his whip he sent her horse flying on its way and, scorning the feeble attempts of her attendants to stop him, turned his horse homeward with a mighty pull on the reins which forced it up on its hind-quarters and made foam fly from its nostrils.

"Marion – my fair Marion!" he chided her. "There is no point in screaming or struggling in this way – be calm, keep quiet and listen to me. I love you, my bonnie lass – I love you! You will find that it is fated you shall be mine. No human power can take you from me now. Do but accept that and your fair face shall rest on a manlier breast than that of Branxholm's beardless heir."

With that he raised her face to his and pressed his lips brutally down on hers. Still holding her before him he thrust his spurs once again into his horse's sides and, with his followers streaming behind him, rode furiously towards Hermitage Castle. Once returned he locked his bride-to-be in a strong but comfortably furnished chamber with bars in the windows which looked out on to the moat. Then he set about trying to persuade her to accept him.

She retaliated at first by weeping piteously, by wringing her hands and imploring his mercy and by begging him to set her free again. Finding these tactics availed not a whit, but that her tears were wasted and her prayers scorned, she turned to defiance invoking the vengeance of Heaven on him. At this the sorcerer stood awestruck in her presence, for there was a natural power in the innocent goodness of that virtuous child – for she was little more – which turned the wizard speechless and gave her a slight respite from his importunities.

On the third night, wearied by the useless struggle to overcome her natural repugnance to him, he seized her in his arms. While his servants were all asleep he carried her down to the dark dungeon, where the sounds of the dying beasts still lingered. Here he hoped to make his evil spirit cast a spell on her to force her to love him.

He placed his lamp on the ground beside the two roughly filled-in graves and the chest. Then holding Marion firmly to his side, where she stood almost overcome with terror, he struck with his mailed fist three times on the lid of the huge iron-bound chest.

"Spirit, come forth," he cried.

Three times three he repeated the blows and each time he uttered the command. But there was no movement of the lid of the chest. No fiendish familiar appeared at his summons.

The wretched Marion, who had heard of his familiar fiend and countless tales of his sorcery, which were well known throughout the countryside, was overcome with terror. Halfway through the proceedings she fainted in his iron grasp. When she recovered she found herself once again in the chamber with the barred windows in which she had previously been held prisoner and Soulis was no longer with her. She did her best to recover herself and knelt to pray that her Walter might be sent to free her from the clutches of the wizard Soulis.

It was barely daybreak when the young heir of Branxholm, Sir Walter Scott, whose bow, it was said, no other man could bend and whose sword was renowned in battle, arrived before the walls of Hermitage Castle with twenty armed men and demanded to speak to the earl of Soulis. The sound of his horn at the gates drew Soulis and his attendants on to the battlements. He looked down at the young knight contemptuously.

"What is it you want, boy, that you arrive before sunrise in such fashion?" asked the wizard earl mockingly. "Do you come to seek the lion in his den?"

"I come in the name of our good King," replied the young heir of Branxholm boldly. "And by his authority I demand that you give up into my hands, safe and sound, my betrothed bride-to-be, or vengeance will surely come upon you."

"Vengeance, indeed, you beardless boy!" taunted the sorcerer. "Who dares to speak of vengeance against the house of Soulis? And who do you call king? The crown is mine and you will also be mine and die the death of a dog for your boasts this morning. To arms! To arms!" he shouted as he turned back from the battlements.

Moments later the gate of the castle opened and a hundred armed men rushed through with the formidable figure of Soulis himself at their head. Sir Walter's small company quailed at the sight of this much superior force backed by the evil powers of Soulis. However, when they saw the confident bearing of their young leader and remembered the strength of his arm and the widespread fear of his sword their hopes revived.

The two sides met in fierce conflict. The superior force of Soulis and his men charged down on Sir Walter and his followers, intent on overcoming them like wolves on a flock of sheep. Nothing could stand in the way of the wizard's sword and his opponents fell right and left in front of him overcome by his enormous strength. Even Walter marvelled at the way the sorcerer hewed his opponents down as he himself pressed forward to meet him.

Before he could reach Soulis, his own remaining followers had fled before the superior numbers of their enemy. He was left to fight on single-handed. All but three of Soulis's followers who remained with their master went in pursuit of Branxholm's fleeing men. Against these three and their wizard master young Walter charged furiously. As they surrounded him, Soulis, relying on his strength and his familiar fiend's promise, ordered his men back.

"Leave him to me," he cried. "Young Branxholm shall meet his death from me alone. It is right that I should take his head on a platter as a wedding present for my bride, the fair Marion."

"Your bride, wizard!" shouted Walter furiously. "Not yours but mine, you fiend!"

With that he attacked the wizard earl with a furious series of sword cuts coming from all angles.

"Ha, now," cried Soulis, parrying his thrusts, but marvelling at the impetuosity of his opponent. "You might as well have sticks as a sword. Steel can have no effect on me!"

"Sorcerer though you may be," panted Walter, pressing on with his attack with undiminished fervour, "this sword will prove you wrong yet and put an end to your magic."

Once more Soulis laughed, but despite his contemptuous dismissal of his young opponent he soon discovered that Walter's strength was equal to his own and in repelling his fierce attacks he almost forgot the charm that preserved him. They fought long and desperately, until one of his followers thrust his long spear into the side of Walter's horse which reared, stumbled and fell to the ground.

"Aha!" exclaimed Soulis triumphantly. "Why did you presume to fight me, boy?"

Leaping from his horse he pressed his iron-shod heel on the chest of his fallen foe and placed the point of his sword at his throat.

"You will not die yet," he decreed.

He turned to the three men who had not joined in the pursuit of the enemy.

"Come now! Tie him up and see he is well secured," he commanded them.

"A coward as well as a wizard," taunted Walter, as he was dragged through the castle gates. "You will regret your treachery yet, I promise you."

"Ha, you boast in vain, boy," replied Soulis contemptuously. "It is you who will regret your recklessness. That I promise you with good reason."

He then ordered his men to take Walter to the door of the chamber where Marion was imprisoned and leave them. Then grasping the younger man by the neck he dragged him into the room. Throwing the bound prisoner in front of her and holding his naked sword point at the young man's throat, he threatened her sternly.

"If you do not now consent to be mine, Marion," he said, "I shall cut off his head and let it roll before you on the floor. If you agree to be mine, I will let the boy live. Say but the word."

"You monster!" she screamed. "Do not harm my poor Walter!"

"Ah, Marion, my Marion!" cried Walter, struggling furiously against the ropes that bound him and glaring fiercely at Soulis. "Kill me, you fiend, but do not harm her."

"Think about it, maiden," cried the wizard. "The life of your bonnie bridegroom depends on your decision. But I will grant you till midnight to think on it. Agree but to be mine then and no harm will come to him or to you. You will have a man for a husband and not this boy I have brought before you bound and helpless."

"Ah, you wretched sorcerer," cried Walter furiously. "If I were but free, unarmed as I am, I would force my way out of your prison with my bride, despite you and your men."

Soulis laughed scornfully at his impotent threats as well he might and once more addressed the half-fainting maiden.

"Think well on what I have said," he continued threateningly, "if you want this young cockerel left alive."

He then dragged her affianced bridegroom to the far corner of her prison chamber and fettered him firmly to the wall with a strong steel chain which he had in readiness for the purpose. Then, picking the lass up with ease, he chained her in a similar manner to the opposite wall, with the difference that the chains he used to bind her with were made of silver. Giving her a final stern warning of what awaited her if she did not agree to his terms he left them together.

When they were left alone Marion wept bitterly at their hopeless situation.

"Do not weep, my love," said Walter stoutly. "And do not think of agreeing to his terms to save me. Before tomorrow our friends will have arrived to rescue you and even if he kills me it is better that I remain your bridegroom in memory rather than you should agree to his vile terms."

"I would rather die with you," agreed Marion with spirit, recovering somewhat from her despair.

Throughout the day the Earl of Soulis found his mood strangely troubled. A sense of impeding danger weighed on his mind. He walked to and fro on the battlements of his castle looking out anxiously for the return of his retainers who had set off in pursuit of the followers of Walter Scott of Branxholm. The sun had set and darkness had fallen but there was still no sign of them and he was becoming increasingly anxious and worried. At last, as it neared midnight, a single horseman spurred his jaded beast towards the castle gate. The Earl of Soulis, impatient for news, opened the gate to the courtyard himself and before the rider had time to dismount he was bombarding him with questions, his voice filled with foreboding. "Why have you returned alone?" he demanded sternly. "And where are your companions? What is your news?"

"Excuse me, my lord," faltered the horseman, dismounting stiffly. "I am the bearer of bad news."

"Bad news, damn you!" cried the Earl impatiently. "Do not speak of bad news to me. What is it? Where are the men who went forth with you?"

The horseman winced as the Earl struck him with his whip, but went on hastily.

"When we followed the men of Branxholm they took refuge in the wilds of Tarras moss," he explained. "We were ignorant of the winding paths through its bottomless morass and most of our horses and men now lie buried in it. Those who did not sink in the bog and those who were unhorsed were killed by the swords of the Branxholm men. I was the only one to escape and my horse is like to die."

"And why did you escape, you knave?" demanded the fierce wizard, striking the man to the ground. "Why did you have to live to tell me of this blot on the house of Soulis's honour?"

Turning on his heel he hurried yet again to the haunted dungeon and again performed his weird incantations impatiently. Rage was betrayed in his lowered brow and tone of voice. Three times three he struck violently with his mailed fist on the iron-bound chest and exclaimed in tones of wrath on each occasion.

"Spirit come forth! Arise and speak with me!"

This time the lid slowly rose with an ominous grating sound and at last fell open with a mighty clang, reverberating like the sound of thunder in the vaulted dungeon. The spirit itself did not appear, but the smell was ten times worse than before, as if a thousand tombs had been opened to yield up the diseased bodies of a multitude. The sepulchral hollow voice, now deeper than before and speaking in tones of anger, echoed round the dungeon.

"Mortal! Wherefore have you summoned me before the time I commanded you? Was your wish not granted? Steel shall not wound you, cords shall not bind you, hemp shall not hang you, nor water drown you. Go!"

"Wait!" cried Soulis urgently. "Add, nor fire consume me!"

"Ah! Ha! Ha! Ha!" cried the spirit, giving vent to a fearful laugh, which made even the wizard tremble at the sound. *"Beware of a coming wood!"*

Then with an even louder clang than before the lid of the chest fell and the sound of subterranean thunder was repeated with long and loud reverberations, which made the dust of the dungeon rise in clouds.

"Beware of a coming wood!" muttered the Earl to himself. "What can that mean?"

He hastened from the dungeon and as he passed through the door he took the key from his belt. Instead of locking it, however, he threw the key over his left shoulder.

"Keep it, spirit!" he shouted furiously. "And confound your riddle!"

The rest of the night he spent in his own chamber trying to work out the meaning of the warning he had received and also pondering the death of his followers. He barely thought of Marion and her bridegroom until day had dawned, when, with a still troubled but wrathful face, he entered their prison.

"Well, now! Have you thought over my words? Will you be my willing bride and let young Scott of Branxholm live? Or do you refuse and prefer to admire his young head spiked on the end of my spear?"

"Rather than see her your bride," exclaimed young

Walter impetuously, "I would prefer you to chop me into pieces and feed them to your hounds."

"Well, that's not a bad suggestion," agreed the wizard, seeming somewhat struck by the proposal. "You may yet have your wish. However, boy, you appear to think I am without mercy. Well, I will teach you that is not the case. Just tell me truly: if I were in your power as you are in mine, what would my fate be in those circumstances?"

"The answer is simple," replied Walter stoutly. "I would hang you from the highest tree in Branxholm Woods."

"Well said, my young sprig," replied Soulis with an evil smile. "And I will show you that I am really more merciful than you. You say you would choose the highest tree for me, but I will *give you the choice of tree from which you shall hang* and on which the ravens may gather for their feast."

He paused for a moment with the same evil smile to savour the thought, then turned towards Marion.

"And since you will not give me your hand, even to save your betrothed," he continued. "If I may not be your husband I will turn priest instead and celebrate your marriage, for I will bind your hand in his and hang you from the next tree."

"For that I thank you," replied the undaunted lass.

Soulis then called his four remaining men and, placing ropes around the necks of his two proposed victims, led them out into the woods around the castle where he proposed that Walter should choose the fatal tree.

Outside the Castle of Hermitage there was a thick mist. They had hardly walked a matter of fifty yards towards the wood where he intended to hang his prisoners than one of his followers exclaimed in amazement.

"What is it?" demanded Soulis impatiently.

"See, my lord. The wood comes towards us," the man replied in amazement.

"What! *The wood comes . . . !*" cried Soulis, and paled as he recalled the words of the demon. *"Beware of a coming wood!"*

For a few moments his heart failed as he remembered the

demon's words. Before he had recovered his presence of mind, four score and more of the followers of Branxholm, each bearing a tall branch of the rowan tree in front of them as a charm against his sorcery, had already surrounded him. With one accord they gave a loud shout and, dropping the branches, drew their swords.

The cords securing Marion and young Walter were severed at once and they were set free. Recovering himself, Soulis drew his sword and with every blow dealt death around him. While his remaining four followers were quickly overpowered or killed, he managed to break through those surrounding him and escape unscathed to the security of his castle once more.

Marion and Walter Scott were content to return to Branxholm where, without delay, they were wed. Meanwhile scarcely a day passed without complaints being received of the Earl of Soulis's continued oppression of his neighbours and the evil practices in which he still indulged. King Robert the Bruce received continual complaints and one day, plagued by more requests for justice than usual, he exclaimed unthinkingly:

"Oh, boil him if you will, but let me hear no more about him!"

Those who had heard his words went away thoughtfully. When they arrived at Hermitage Castle it was to find men of Branxholm fighting with him yet again, but failing to injure him with their swords and spears which simply blunted on his body and did not even wound him. When they overwhelmed him by weight of numbers and attempted to bind him, the ropes simply snapped and failed to hold him. Fortunately they had a wise man skilled in combatting witchcraft and spells accompanying them.

"Wrap him in lead," advised the wise man. "Then boil him as the King decreed, for water and cords of hemp have no power over his spells."

Some of those present ran into the castle and tore the lead from the roof. Holding the wizard down, they wrapped him in folds of lead until he was held powerless and foaming at the mouth in rage. Others found a large cauldron

26

in which many of his spells had been performed. The cry arose:

"Boil him on the Nine-stane rig!"

They carried him up the hill to where the stones of the Druids are still to be seen. Even today the local people may point out the stones from which the cauldron was suspended. Underneath it they piled loads of fresh faggots and then, bending the Earl's body wrapped in the folded lead, they thrust it into the cauldron. As the flames arose around the cauldron the lead melted slowly and the bones of the wizard were consumed by the boiling lead. Such was the doom of Soulis.

It is small wonder that Hermitage Castle still has about it an aura of something not quite canny, as the locals term it. The Earl of Soulis's reputation in itself was enough to leave an uncanny feeling behind on the spot where he performed so many evil deeds. On the hill where the Druid stones still stand they say that as darkness falls on every anniversary of the day the doom of Soulis took place you can still hear the agonised howlings of the wizard Earl of Hermitage echoing around the hills.

Five-and-a-half miles north of Castleton and some fifteen miles south of Hawick, Hermitage Castle is still an impressive, if forbidding, ruin standing isolated in the hills, but now in the care of the Ministry of Ancient Monuments. Guardian of one of the main approaches to Scotland through Liddesdale, it has a bloody history apart from the legendary exploits of the Earl of Soulis.

THE LAIRD OF DARNICK

On Bruce's death in 1329 his son was still a child of
only five years of age. It was to be Scotland's misfortune, time after time, to have a minor succeed to the
throne at critical periods in her history. It was a further
source of ill-fortune that she was fated all too often to
have weak rulers when the need for a strong hand was
paramount. For much of the next three hundred years
there was also to be an intermittent struggle for power
amongst the more prominent noble families in the
land. The Earls of Douglas, the Black Douglases, and
the Earls of Angus, the Red Douglases, and the Lennox
Stewarts were all related to the Scottish Crown by marriage, as well as being frequently inter-related amongst
themselves. Other powerful noble families, such as
that of Walter Scott of Buccleuch, were also related to
them. In such circumstances it is scarcely surprising
that Scotland's history and that of the Borders area in
particular is tumultuous and even chaotic at times.

Until his death at Flodden in 1513 along with the
flower of the Scottish nobility, James IV had reigned
for twenty-five years. During that time Scotland had
experienced a steady upsurge in trade and prosperity
as well as a welcome return to the rule of law. In 1513
his son, James V, was still only a babe of eighteen
months and the ensuing years inevitably saw a struggle
for power amongst the nobility with the Douglases in
the ascendant. In such circumstances it was under-

standably difficult for minor lairds to know which side
it was politic to follow.

IN 1526 during the youth of King James V, while he
remained a minor under the control of the Earl of Angus,
the Red Douglas, the Borders were riven with strife as
seldom before or since. Faction leagued against faction, no
man's cattle were safe from his neighbour. Border reiving
was a way of life and a strong sword arm and a stout heart
were all that many felt was required to survive. Yet though
that may have been enough for the average Borderer with
nothing to lose but his life, it was not so simple for the minor
lairds, who were inevitably forced to side with one or other
of the larger groups, even though their hearts or their heads
suggested another course.

It was often enough a difficult matter to plot a sensible
course through the maze of conflicting but binding
loyalties. The Laird of Darnick, Andrew Heiton, was in just
such a predicament at this time. His father had fallen at
Flodden and he remained loyal to King James, but he had
seen Walter Scott of Buccleuch rise from a mere reiver to
great power and had ridden on many a reiving expedition
with him. However, he hated the Douglases, who had the
young Prince in their power, and felt bound to ally himself
with his old friend Walter Scott against them.

Despite the fact that James V was still a minor under
the influence and virtually the prisoner of the Earl of
Angus, the Borders were split into supporters either of the
King's party or of the Douglases. Some of the principal
Border leaders, such as Walter Scott of Buccleuch and Elliot
of Stobs, were on the King's side, while the Homes, the Kers
and the Cockburns sided with the Douglases. The Laird of
Darnick, being strongly on the side of the King and of the
Scotts, had hitherto found no real conflict of loyalties.

The young King in the charge of the Earl of Angus was
at that time journeying from Jedburgh to Melrose, passing
within easy reach of Darnick Tower, only a mile to the west,
so Andrew Heiton decided it would be a politic move for

him to join the Royal party despite the fact that the Red Douglas, as Governor, would be present with the young Prince. Calling his retainers together, mounted on their shaggy but sure-footed garrons and making as good a show as they could, he set off to join the King's cavalcade. It was only on his arrival that to his surprise he saw no sign of his friend Walter Scott.

"Where is Wat Scott?" he enquired of several of the Royal party. "Why is he not here with all his followers to show the King the power he is in these parts, fully capable of aiding him against the Douglases and putting an end to their control over the throne?"

No one seemed to know the answer. Some suggested that the changeable Wat Scott of Buccleuch had joined Angus and turned against the young King. Others suggested he was afraid of Angus's power and kept away because of that. Yet others indicated that he might be away in the west or the south on a reiving expedition, taking advantage of the absence of the landowners with the King's party.

These various suggestions interested the Laird of Darnick considerably and gave him much food for thought. He even began to regret his decision to join the Royal party, for it occurred to him that this might cause Wat Scott to turn against him one day. He could just as easily have maintained his loyalty to the King without endangering his ties with the Scotts. However, now that he had committed himself he felt he could only stay and see whether Wat Scott joined them after all.

While he was wondering whether he had taken the right course or not, a faithful retainer arrived from Darnick Tower with a message from his wife.

"The mistress of Darnick says to stand by James Stuart," he whispered in the master's ear.

"And so I intended," grunted the Laird of Darnick, turning to face his servant, Will. "Did Jessie tell you this herself, Will?"

"Aye," replied Will, looking round to see they were not overheard. "And what's more she says Wat Scott is against

James Stuart and that if Buccleuch were ten times the reiver he is, she would still not consent to desert the King."

"That's just like the woman!" replied the laird. "It's not the first time she's got at the truth. Get back to her as fast as you can and let her know I'll be back. I am for the King regardless too."

"And there's more," went on Will remorselessly.

"Isn't that enough?" demanded Heiton. "Get on with it then!"

"There's to be a battle at Darnick; for Wat Scott is planning to take the King at Halidon Hill. You're to come home quick and be ready to offer the tower as a refuge and if necessary defend it, but if you won't, she says she'll defend it herself!"

"Then take this answer with you," retorted the laird. "Say I will return as soon as I can reasonably get away without creating a suspicion of going over to Scott. Meanwhile get everything at the tower ready for a fight. I know she can do all that as well as I could myself, but just tell her to get on with it!"

The messenger slipped away at once and had scarcely gone when Heiton was approached by another man whom he recognised as one of Wat Scott's retainers.

"Why are you here, man," Andrew Heiton challenged him, "when your master is gathering his clan for treason against his King?"

"I am here to seek your help as well as that of some others," replied the man. "My master Walter Scott sends his greetings and says that tomorrow night by God's Grace he intends to surprise the Douglas and seize him and confine him in his castle until the Prince has a better governor or can reign himself, and you are to meet him with all the strength you can muster at Halidon Hill."

"You lie in your teeth, man!" retorted Heiton forthrightly. "It is the King your master wants and then he will rule Scotland and all of us. Go and tell him that, though I hate Angus and his followers, I stand by the King and if he will forget this scheme I will still stand by him."

31

With this answer, which seemed to surprise the messenger, he withdrew and Heiton continued with the cavalcade. He was, however, a somewhat worried man. His wife, he knew, was very seldom wrong. Scott, on the other hand, was an old wolf who was willing to change course to suit his own ends. With him self-interest and what he could gain from it dictated his every course of action. Honesty and loyalty had little to do with it.

While he was still puzzling as to what course to follow a knight in the royal retinue rode close to him and whispered as if afraid of being overheard.

"Heiton!" he murmured. "If you are for the King join Walter Scott."

"The devil take you too," thought Andrew Heiton to himself. "This is surely another trick of Wat Scott's." Like most Borderers of the day he was not long in making up his mind. Prompt, fiery and resolute as well as brave and intrepid, his aid was always courted by the rival clans whenever a desperate enterprise was in the offing. Now, leaving his men behind him, he set his spurs to his horse and galloped over the moors to Darnick as fast as the beast could carry him.

He knew by this time that there was trouble brewing close to his own home at Darnick and the results could be good or bad for him and his. He might either lose his head or win a charter. One thing was certain – in any struggle involving royalty or a Douglas and the Scotts on his doorstep he would not be allowed to remain neutral.

He had barely covered half the distance when he encountered a large body of armed Borderers and realised he was amongst the followers of Wat Scott himself. In a few moments he was facing him on horseback.

"Where are you off to, man?" asked Buccleuch. "As if the Mistress of Darnick waited for you to fetch a heifer from our enemy the Home's parks?"

"With only a small peel tower," replied Andrew Heiton, with a grim smile. "It behoves me to look after it when a thousand Scotts are on the march. It is not for a single heifer that Buccleuch marches with so many and not sounding his horn! May I take the liberty of asking why you are not with the King's cavalcade?"

"Because I wish to do better for my King than follow him," replied Wat Scott.

"It is said that you want to make him follow you!" retorted Heiton boldly. "But though I have no objection to following you I would not want to see my King in the same position."

"Nor will you, man!" replied Scott. "What would Wat Scott do with a King? Let James Stuart keep north and Buccleuch south and there will be no strife in Scotland but that of the good old reiving custom. Come, I want you and your friends!"

"I must know the foray intended first!" replied Heiton stoutly.

"And so you shall," replied Scott. "I know that the young King wants to get out of the grasp of Angus and I wish to undo the grasp."

"But if you fail, our heads may lick the sawdust," replied Heiton. "I must be off to Darnick Tower."

"When will you return?" demanded Scott.

"I will tell you when I know what's happening at Darnick," replied Heiton, spurring his horse once again and this time not drawing rein until he arrived at the tower gate.

"What has brought you here, man, when the King needs you?" asked his wife as he entered the tower. "You look as if the King's headsman was after you and not you after his enemies. Did you see my messenger, Will?"

"I did indeed, Jessie," he replied. "But there are wheels within wheels and others within them in this business."

"And have you lost your wits within the wheels?" she demanded. "For you may even yet lose your head under an axe!"

"And it is because I am afraid of just that I have returned," he replied. "You are wrong, Jessie. Scott wants only to free the King from Douglas. What should I do? If I go with the King I go against Wat Scott and may see the Heading Hill at Stirling. If I go with Scott I go against Douglas and may lose my head even sooner."

33

"Get back to your men as soon as you can!" replied his wife swiftly. "Then bring them back to Darnick as fast as your spurs will bring you. There's no fear of you being suspected of disloyalty for Douglas does not know that Scott is at the back of Halidon Hill. But mind that you keep out of Scott's way as you return, for he has a trick of keeping hold of livestock when they pass his way!"

"And what am I to do when I return?" demanded Heiton. "For if there's a fight at Darnick the Laird of Darnick will be expected to be in the thick of it, surely?"

"So you will be, man," she cried. "But mount and go now as fast as you can and do what I say!"

Without waiting for further discussion, Heiton rode off again as fast as he could by a roundabout route to rejoin the Royal cavalcade, which was now approaching the dangerous area. Signalling to his followers to follow him he took the same route at speed back to Darnick Tower. Once there he had little time to lose, for already there were signs of the approaching Royal procession.

The Mistress of Darnick then set her plans in motion. The men were sent on various errands to keep them busy so as not to be readily available unless summoned. The door of the peel tower was bolted and locked and, after she had explained her plans to him, Heiton himself retired to the inner hall, where he could hear what went on but not be seen. His wife then climbed to the topmost point of the tower where she could watch without being seen herself.

She had barely completed these preparations when the tramp of horses' hooves could be heard. Then came the sound of trumpets which the heralds blew as the town of Melrose came into sight. The heraldic banners glittered in the sun and the armour of the knights and barons glinted in its rays. The young Prince, James Stuart, was in the lead on horseback between Angus on the one side and George Douglas on the other. The procession, with all the panoply of royalty, presented a peaceful demonstration of the power of the King.

34

Then out of the hills came the blast of a horn accompanied by the sound of the Scott's war cry of "Bellenden!" and a wild Border cheer as a thousand wild Borderers armed with swords, two-headed Jedhart axes and spears came charging forward on their shaggy garrons, rushing like a flood on the unprepared Royal procession. Leading the attack was Walter Scott, stern of face and fierce of eye.

A phalanx was formed about the King and the Douglases, mad with the fear of losing their Royal prize, cried, "For the King! For the King!" This was answered with repeated shouts from the Scotts and battle was joined with the fury of hope on one side and the rage of despair in the other. At the start the surprise of the Borderers' attack and the sheer pressure of it gave them the advantage. As their hopes rose so the pressure increased and repeated shouts amongst the clanging of sword on sword and the thud of the falling axes told of their success.

Wat Scott himself appeared to be everywhere in the forefront, shouting to secure the Prince and hacking with his sword. Gradually, however, the Douglases recovered themselves and the battle became a mass of fighting men, breathing hard and hacking with their swords, axes or spears. Then once more the battle seemed to turn in Buccleuch's favour and the shouts of "Bellenden! Bellenden!" began to rise again.

Suddenly, however, there came a renewed cheer from the King's party even though they were falling back. The reason was soon plain. Two parties of the Homes and Kers had that moment arrived, eager to revenge themselves on their old enemies, the Scotts. The onset of the newcomers was fierce and clearly soon to be decisive.

All this had been watched by the Mistress of Darnick and listened to by Andrew Heiton with the frustration of a caged lion. But now his time had come, for it was impossible for Buccleuch to win against these fresh odds.

"Now," cried Jessie Heiton, Mistress of Darnick. "Now go, my lord. You know whom to fight for. In a short while the King's party will be triumphant. Get into the thick of the fight, but as far from Wat Scott as you can. Thus you will save your head and your land without injuring your old friend."

The gates of Darnick opened and Andrew Heiton was soon fighting strenuously in the ranks of the King, his arm dealing death at every stroke. "Heiton to the rescue!" was sounded on his horn and those of his retainers gathered at hand took the Scotts in the flank. The action was decisive. In a short time the Scotts were in full retreat and the wounded of the King's party were carried to Darnick Tower, where the Heitons' hospitality was soon to the fore.

The Mistress of Darnick's masterly policy had saved the Tower and its master's head. Walter Scott of Buccleuch was outlawed and all who had taken part on his side severely punished. Those who had not come forward in support of Angus were likewise out of favour. For Andrew Heiton a fresh charter to the lands of Darnick was reward enough. Being on the very site of the battle, he was well aware that he could easily enough have lost everything but for his wife's discernment.

Darnick Tower still stands one mile west of Melrose, an ancient and impressive fortress dating from the thirteenth century with later additions. It has now very suitably been turned into a Museum of Border Antiquities and is well worth visiting.

Melrose itself is an attractive small town and Melrose Abbey is one of the finest of the Border abbeys, much pillaged during the various English invasions. This is a useful base for touring the Scott country.

THE MAIDEN FEAST
OF CAIRNKIBBIE

James V was seventeen in 1530 before he escaped from the clutches of the Douglases, but once his own master he soon imposed his will on the country. The Douglases were the first to suffer and were ultimately banished to England. The Borders too soon felt his strong hand. Two powerful Border chieftains, Adam Scott of Tushielaw and Cockburn of Henderland, were hanged in Edinburgh. The most notorious Border outlaw, however, was John Armstrong of Caerlanrig, near Teviothead, who plundered the English side of the Border continually, though equally happy to raid and pillage on the Scottish side, being credited with having sacked over fifty Scottish churches.

The young King assembled a hunting party of over a thousand men and either promised Armstrong a safe-conduct, or the latter felt it wise to appear and swear fealty with twenty-five of his chief followers. Whatever the circumstances, the young King had them all instantly seized, bound and hung out of hand. The power of the Armstrongs was broken thereafter but the ballad of Johnnie Armstrong indicates that there was considerable popular sympathy for the reiver. Such severe measures, however, quickly restored the rule of law in the land.

But there was another side to James. He enjoyed

going about in disguise and meeting the people and was sometimes called "The Poor Man's King." The following tale shows something of this side of the man.

IN THE early sixteenth century during the early days of the reign of James V, before the Reformation laid its restraining influence on them, the Border harvest homes, or Maiden Feasts as they were termed, were often very wild and immensely enjoyable parties which started early in the evening and went on all night, with dancing, drinking, kissing and the sound of music and laughter. The neighbouring farmers and their farm staff all attended and in due course invited their neighbours in return, so that many a fine entertainment resulted in the autumn months once the harvest was safely gathered in. The Maiden Feast of Cairnkibbie, a farm on the property of Faulden farmed by William Hume, was known far and wide. His daughter Lilly Hume was a particularly delightful lass, as beautiful as she was polite and pleasing in her approach to everyone she met. Even those neighbouring lasses who might have envied her for her looks were happy to know and admire her for her natural friendly manners to all and sundry.

The Maiden Feast of Cairnkibbie was well under way with the blind piper playing the tunes while a crock of ale was kept well filled beside him to give him aid and inspiration. Many young couples were dancing energetically, while others were laughing, cuddling and kissing, telling jokes or sitting in corners drinking toasts to each other, while their elders either watched with enjoyment, or joined in the general frolic or dancing. It was a scene of merriment and general gaiety almost unequalled by any of the other Maiden Feasts as the couples clapped their hands, shouted and squared up to their partners, or skirled round the floor arm in arm, with their feet seeming to scarcely touch the boards.

At one point there was something of a dispute between two of the most presentable young men present, namely Jock Hedderick and Will Aitken. This concerned the application of a gaberlunzie, or beggar, who announced his presence at the main door of the barn and demanded entry on the grounds of the ancient right of the beggars of Scotland to gain entry to any Maiden Feast being held. Jock Hedderick disputed any such right while Will Aitken backed the beggar. At one point the dispute seemed to be in danger of growing fierce, but finally the gaberlunzie himself prevailed, thrusting his way through the doors into the barn where the feast was being held.

He was carrying various large packs, but as soon as he was inside the door he dropped these in a corner and gave such a loud and reverberating laugh that the music was drowned for a few moments. Everyone who heard it was tempted to join in so infectious a sound of merriment directed as much at himself as at those arguing for and against his entry. Then, taking up his pipes, he began to play such a joyous and merry air that everyone fell to dancing and even the sober Will Hume and his wife were seen treading the boards with the rest. Meanwhile the old blind piper, glad of a rest, was taking his fill from the crock beside him.

When the gaberlunzie had played several catchy airs with such tempestuous feeling and excitement that everyone who was not dancing had been humming the tunes, he at last fell silent and let his pipes drop.

"That has made me dry," he cried in a loud voice which filled the room. "Now what about some ale?"

When the stoup of ale was brought to him he poured it back in one great draught without stopping for breath so that everyone present stood amazed at his drinking abilities. But not content with that single draught he refilled his crock and once again drained it at one go, following this feat with a mighty laugh which set everyone smiling or laughing with him.

"Come now, let us all be dancing again," he cried, and seizing his pipes once more he set such a rousing tune going that all the dancers who had thought themselves exhausted again started to whirl their partners in a reel, while the skirling pipes urged them to ever greater efforts. Finally the gaberlunzie threw down his pipes and, taking another vast draught of ale, shouted out to the blind piper to take over the piping while he took his place in the dancing. The blind piper, by this time recovered from his earlier efforts, willingly obliged and seizing the fair Lilly the gaberlunzie stepped out on the floor.

"And who is your man, my dear?" he asked her directly.

"It's Will Carr, yonder," she replied. "But my father says I must not dance with him."

"Oh, so he does, does he indeed?" cried the beggar. "And why is that?"

"He says he has no money," replied the artless girl, with a natural simplicity.

"Is that so, and here you are dancing with another of the same kind!" he cried with a laugh. "But I see no objection from your father on that account."

Indeed the gaberlunzie had introduced such life and sparkle to the Maiden Feast that what had previously been a thoroughly enjoyable, but not unusual, evening had suddenly gained a new dimension. He danced around the room, hardly seeming to stop for an instant, taking partners from all ages, from the douce Mrs Hume herself, who was soon laughing and blushing like the veriest maiden, to the youngest lass on the floor. He kissed them all with a gay abandon, from grandmothers to maidens, and kept them all smiling and laughing at his jokes.

When the old blind piper tired of his labours, the gaberlunzie gathered a crowd around him and told such outrageous stories with such infectious laughter that he had the whole crowd in fits and everyone bursting their sides with laughter. Then seizing the pipes himself yet again he blew them fit to burst and set everyone a-dancing just when they had vowed that they were too tired for more. Once again after half a dozen reels he passed the piping back to the old blind piper, who was inspired to copy the efforts of his rival and played in a way no one had heard before, with an abandon almost like the other. Meanwhile the beggar had set up a dance with Bess Gordon, one of the more handsome local lasses. She could not, however, hold a candle to the fair Lilly Hume.

"Here now, Will Carr," cried the gaberlunzie. "It's your turn here."

With that he passed Bess Gordon over to Will Carr and seized Lilly Hume herself once more, but in a few moments he had changed back with a hissed command to Will Carr and Lilly to "make the most" of their chances. Then he himself was off round the barn still behaving in the most extraordinary fashion, kissing Will Hume's wife with an outrageous abandon and whirling Will Hume himself in a turn about the floor. A moment later he was off for a turn with Bess Gordon or another of the lasses on the floor of the barn.

"Look after the blind piper, my lads," he cried. "If you don't give him ale enough he'll not keep you treading the boards. Give us the *Hunts of Cheviot,* lad!"

The piper willingly enough struck up the new dance to be followed at the gaberlunzie's shouts with another and yet another as the music ended. Everyone in the barn was inspired to a pitch of near frenzy by the laughing, dancing gaberlunzie, who seemed to be here, there and everywhere, charming each of them with a joke, a kiss, a dance or a fresh stoup of ale. As the night wore on he seemed merely to increase his activities, dancing and piping or drinking and joking without cease and all the time finding his way to the hearts of all those present.

"Keep at it, Will," he cried as he passed Will Carr still dancing with Lilly Hume. "You'll have all you want of Lilly this night, or my name's not Wat Wilson."

His name was soon being bandied round the room for, with the perspiration streaming from his forehead, he had already become everyone's favourite. Not a soul in the room but had exchanged jokes, a toast, a dance or a kiss with the man who seemed to be everywhere at once. The whole pace and enjoyment of the evening owed almost everything to him and William Hume himself, more than anyone, was charmed by the remarkable abilities the gaberlunzie

41

showed. Surely no man had such amazing ability to drink, to laugh, tell jokes and dance, or charm the opposite sex as this man Wat Wilson? His lungs seemed of leather for he kept the pipes going tirelessly, but when the dancers were wearied he drank and told such jokes that everyone crowded round him to hear and screamed with laughter at each fresh sally.

Then abruptly there was the sound of horses outside and a knock at the barn door. A sudden cry went up that there were armed men come to demand a thief who had that day stolen the silver mace of King James at Duns. It was suspected that he was at this dance in the disguise of a wandering piper.

"That is the man!" cried a knight, who strode into the hall with his sword at his side, pointing a finger at the happy gaberlunzie who had just finished a song.

"That's a lie!" replied the beggar instantly, standing up surrounded by his new friends.

"Ha, now! This boldness will not help you," cried the knight. "Your new-found friends here will not save you. I know you and there are witnesses who saw you steal the mace. Come in, sirs, and identify this man!"

Two more knights entered behind the first at this cry.

"Is he not the thief?" demanded the inquisitor.

"It is indeed. We can swear to him," they replied together. "He snatched the mace from the royal mace-bearer in the High Street of Duns and made off with it amidst the hue and cry of all the people present."

"I'm not surprised at that," remarked Will Hume of Cairnkibbie. "If he ran as cleverly as he danced this evening all the greyhounds in the Merse would not have caught him."

"Will you give me up to these beadles, my friends?" cried the gaberlunzie. "Or will you stand by him who has sought your protection and partaken of your hospitality?"

"Give you up!" cried an old farmer. "By my faith, never! If King James had seven times as many crowns we'll not let you go while we've a flail in the place to defend you."

A general shout of agreement echoed through the barn and everyone reached for a rake or flail to act as a weapon.

"We'll defend him to our last breath," cried Will Carr, brandishing an oak stick.

"And so say all of us!" cried Jock Hedderick.

"And I'm beside you too!" shouted Will Aitken, brandishing a rake beside his friend and rival.

"Ha, ha, good men and true, good men and true," cried the gaberlunzie, laughing loudly and not a whit abashed. "Thank you for your support. Come on then, you silver-necklaced bulldogs of royalty, what will you do now?"

"Search his wallet!" cried the knight who had first entered, and six or seven men rushed into the room and headed for the window sill where the beggar's packs were lying. However, Will Carr and Will Aitken, flanked by Jock Hedderick and half a dozen more, opposed them and held them back.

"Let me have my packs," cried the gaberlunzie with a roar of laughter.

Having got hold of them, to everyone's amazement he pulled one open and produced the silver mace which was said to have been stolen. Holding it in his left hand like a badge of authority, he continued laughing loudly.

"Beggars have a king as well as belted knights," he cried. "See here my badge. Do you not know who you seek? I am Wat Wilson, king of the gaberlunzies, crowned on Hogmanay on Warlock Hill near Duns in the presence of all the tribes of beggars and gaberlunzies from Berwick to Lerwick. This is the beggar's badge. Take it if you dare."

"Now, William Hume of Cairnkibbie," said the leading knight. "You see the evidence in this bold beggar's own hand that he has stolen a part of the King's regalia, which is an act of high treason incurring death to him and all that give him shelter. If you try to rescue him and I report it, King James will punish you and all these misguided people will be ruined along with you. You will bitterly regret having harboured and defended such a thief and vagabond. Will you give him up or must we take him with bloodshed on both sides?"

43

"That's all very well!" replied the farmer. "But this gaberlunzie is our guest. He says the bauble is his and I'm bound to say that King James himself could not be more king of the land than this man king of his tribe. Every inch of him's a king. He dances like a king, he sings like a king, he jokes like a king, he pipes like a king and he kisses the lasses like a king and this night we have been his loyal subjects. As such we'll stand by him. What say you all, my friends?"

"Aye, we're with you, Will," the cries of the dancers at the Maiden Feast resounded. "We're with you."

"On your own heads be it," replied the knight. "Draw for King James and let's have that man a prisoner."

The men outside entered with drawn swords, clearly expected the sight of naked steel to overcome all resist-ance, but the farm workers, with their long flails and rakes and stout cudgels, were not so easily cowed. With some stout blows they soon forced the knights to keep their distance, although the latter were not ready to draw blood and were content simply to parry the blows aimed at them and advance slowly as the farmers hastily slipped all the women folk out of the back door. While all this was going on, the gaberlunzie was sliding in and out of his supporters whispering instructions and, gradually, as the knights advanced the farm workers retreated. Then, at a cry from the gaberlunzie they turned and fled in a solid group through the back doors, which were then slammed and bolted in the advancing knights' faces. The King's men turned back to the front door by which they had entered but found this also barred and bolted, so that they were locked in the barn. In vain they roared threats through the chinks in the doors and demanded to be let out. The gaberlunzie responded to all their cries with cutting irony and even set his pipes swelling in a paean of triumph at his success, drowning all their shouts completely.

"You may tell your king, when you get out," he cried in the silence that followed when he ended with a final trium-phant skirl of the pipes, "that he is not the only king in these realms and surely Scotland is large enough for two. I have my subjects and he has his. And Wat Wilson is not the potentate who would interfere with James Stuart if James Stuart will leave Wat Wilson alone. If I happen to pass Duns in the morning I will not forget to report on your prowess favourably!"

He then turned to the gathering from the Maiden Feast who were crowded round him, still laughing at his sallies.

"Come now, my friends," he addressed them, "let us adjourn the feast to the hall and leave these knights to take their night's rest in the barn after their desperate battle."

There was a loud shout of acclaim at this, but William Hume noticed to his surprise there was no blustering or swearing of vengeance from the imprisoned knights. Their sudden imprisonment seemed to have overcome their spirits completely and the old farmer was at a loss to understand why this should be. When he put this question to the gaberlunzie he gave a great laugh and attributed it to his magical powers and the awe his name inspired throughout Scotland.

"This is the most extraordinary devil that it has ever been my fortune to meet," the farmer thought to himself. "His powers of dancing, roaring, rioting, drinking, piping, singing, joking and fighting all seem to be about equal and above all he seems able to win the hearts of young and old. He has made me like him, and my daughter Lilly and my wife Jean, and now the Maiden Feast has broken up and my barn is full of the King's knights and I have put my head in a noose, all for the sake of a wandering beggar with the boldest tongue I ever met and yet so insinuating that it encouraged the men who wanted to keep him out to let him in and has now got me into the biggest scrape of my life. What on earth am I to do now?"

Thinking thus and sobering up every moment as his fears increased, he looked round for the gaberlunzie to ask him what he had to say, but could not see him in the crowd around.

"Where's that gaberlunzie?" he demanded.

"Where's Wat Wilson?" cried Will Carr.

"Where's that beggar?" cried Will Aitken.

Look where they might there was no sign of him. Then Jock Hedderick told of how he heard someone riding off on one of the knight's horses and thought at the time it was just someone trying out the mettle of one of the beasts for a short ride. Now it was clear that it was the gaberlunzie who had ridden off, taking his packs, his pipes and the stolen mace with him and crowning his extraordinary behaviour that evening by stealing one of the King's horses as well.

It was soon apparent to everyone present that their situation was desperate and that farmer William Hume was in the most parlous position of them all, for not only had he aided and abettted the beggar, but he had acted as spokesman and defied the forces of law and order. Some offered to try to catch the gaberlunzie, but it was obvious to everyone that if someone who could dance and pipe and drink like he had done could also ride, then by this time he was probably well beyond the reach of any present. Others suggested getting help in case the knights broke free. Yet others were for letting the knights go free to pursue the beggar, on the condition they did not try to revenge themselves for their treatment. This seemed the best idea, especially as they could include the loss of the horse in any such deal. William Hume therefore approached the main door of the barn.

"We wish to be friendly disposed towards you," he cried in a voice they could hear within the barn. "It was yon accursed gaberlunzie was your foe, not us. The man must be the very Devil himself, for it was he who encouraged us to take up arms and defy the lawful servants of the King. Now he's up and gone and left us to pay the piper. Well, we're all peaceful folk and we just wanted to know the terms you'll make if we were to open the doors and set you free?"

To the surprise of all present the answer from inside the barn was a loud burst of prolonged laughter.

"That's all very well," said the farmer. "You may laugh now, but you may not laugh when you get out. This may be a ruse to get us to open the doors. Will you promise to let us alone if we let you out?"

46

"We will promise!" was the reply with another laugh.

"That's well enough then," continued the farmer. "And mind I have witnesses who heard you give your word. But I am sorry also to have to tell you that the devil who stole the mace also went off with the best horse of those you left outside. Will you forgive us that as well?"

Another loud laugh sounded from within the barn and there were cries of: "Come along now, open the door." "Never mind the horse. Let's be out of here." "Let the king of the beggars have his horse for he deserves it!"

"Well, well," murmured the farmer. "These are the most pleasant enemies I've ever dealt with. Just hold on to your sticks, my friends, in case they decide to change their tune when they come out."

The farm workers stood round gripping their rakes and flails as the farmer released the bolts on the door, but when the knights came out they were still laughing and joking amongst themselves. Nor were they content with accepting the terms of the treaty agreed. Slapping William Hume on the back they proposed that as they had broken up the evening's festivities they should start them off again and that each knight would take part in a dance with at least one of the maidens they had seen when they first arrived.

This request was greeted with applause from all concerned and the blind piper was once more set to work. The ale was brought out and flowed again as before. In a short while the knights were taking the floor and dancing with the assembled lasses. Despite their best efforts, however, no-one present could help but feel that their dancing and attempts at high spirits did not begin to compare with the performance of the gaberlunzie.

The knights did not stay too long, but mounted their horses, along with one supplied by William Hume to make up for the stolen one, and after a final stirrup cup, departed. The Maiden Feast itself did not long survive their departure. Everyone was fairly exhausted by the evening's events and the farmer, although his fears were somewhat abated, was still worried about how his conduct might be viewed by the King's deputies.

In the morning his worst fears were quickly revived. About eleven o'clock a horseman, booted and spurred, arrived in great haste at the door of the farmhouse of Cairn-kibbie and demanded to see William Hume.

"What is your will, sir?" asked the farmer of this messenger.

"I bear His Majesty the King's schedule, to be delivered to William Hume, the tenant of Cairnkibbie," he replied.

"The King's schedule!" said William Hume. "What has it to say?"

"Read it," commanded the messenger.

William Hume opened the document and read as follows:

"Whereas a gaberlunzie, by name Wat Wilson, a wandering vagabond of that name, did steal our silver mace from the hands of our mace bearer in the town of Duns yesterday wherewith he fled treacherously to the protection and refuge of you, William Hume, tenant of Cairnkibbie, who with your tenants, domestics and retainers did harbour and shelter him against my officers of justice, who you did pummel and ill use in a most shameful manner and thereafter did confine in a barn while the said gaberlunzie stole one of our very choicest horses, for all that you shall answer at our ambulatory court in the old burgh of Duns whereto you are summoned on the day after you receive this missive at twelve in the forenoon, which if you disregard you shall be duly punished by our writ. Given at Duns James R."

"The Lord have mercy on the house of Cairnkibbie," cried the farmer after reading this wrathful missive. "How can I face the King after abusing his officers and harbouring the thief who stole his mace and his officer's horse? Can you help me, sir, and advise me what to do in this awful situation?"

The messenger seemed sympathetic. Looking up, he saw the fair Lilly standing in the doorway. He smiled as if a thought had struck him.

"Is that your daughter?" he asked.

"It is indeed," replied the wretched farmer. "But that has nothing to do with the question in hand."

"It may have more than you think," replied the messenger. "Take her with you to court. The King can never resist the appeal of a beautiful face."

With these words the messenger spurred his horse and departed, leaving the farmer in a miserable state of fright. Will Hume returned to the house and reported the result of his interview to his wife and daughter.

His wife Jean was determined not to allow him to go to his fate at Duns without her and Lilly agreed to accompany them. They also planned to take Will Carr and some of the farm hands as witnesses for the defence, for the farmer had decided on making a clean breast of matters. The truth, he felt, might just get him out of bother whereas any attempt at concealing matters could only lead to trouble.

At an early hour next day they prepared to leave for Duns. The farmer had on his best blue coat and bonnet, his wife her best bonnet and gown and Lilly her best gown and bonnet also. On their arrival at the town of Duns two officials met them and claimed them in the King's name, taking them to a small castle at the end of the town used then as a garrison for the King's troops. They were led down a long corridor and finally entered a large state apartment hung with gorgeous rich cloth. There they were told to sit down on a long bench. Around them were numerous individuals in fine court clothes and, in front of them on a raised dais, sat King James V with three or four barons sitting beneath him. All was portentous silence for some minutes then a voice called out:

"William Hume!"

"Here," replied the farmer in a choked voice, while his wife and daughter shivered in their seats.

"Stand up, sir," cried the same voice.

William duly stood up and the voice of His Majesty resounded through the hall.

"Read the charges," cried the King.

The same indictment he had already received was then read.

"Is it true," demanded the King, "that you harboured this man Wat Wilson knowing him to have stolen our mace and thereafter did beat and confine our messengers sent to apprehend him?"

Like many others in a similar situation, although at first frightened out of his wits, William Hume regained his self-possession as soon as he was asked a plain question.

"I came here today," he replied, looking up with increasing confidence, "to tell Your Majesty the plain truth and I cannot deny the charge."

"Have you anything to say at all in mitigation of the charge then?" demanded the King.

"Overmuch, I fear, Your Majesty," replied the farmer.

"For when I look back on the madness of that night I have almost come to the conclusion that that gaberlunzie, who caused all this trouble, was none other than his august Majesty who –" and he paused uncertainly.

"Who, who?" demanded the King impatiently, while several of the Lords began to laugh behind their hands.

"None other than his august Majesty," went on William, regaining confidence, "who holds his court there." And he pointed downwards dramatically with his finger. "To be plain, Your Majesty, I do believe he was the Devil himself."

The King gave a hearty laugh and the assembled barons all burst into laughter also.

"Come, man!" said the King, recovering himself. "Do you really believe he was the Devil?"

"Indeed I do," replied William, stubbornly, in the face of the laughter still sounding in his ears. "The more I think about it the surer I am. It's the only explanation."

"What did he do to make you so sure of this?" demanded the King. "It would ill behove me to punish a subject for the acts of the Evil One."

"What did he not do?" replied the farmer. "He did everything the Devil could and no man possibly could. First of all we were determined not to let him join the Maiden Feast, but he had us all agreeing to let him in within a few moments. Then he played the part of a man as no man ever could. He drank as no man ever could drink. He danced as no man could dance and made others dance for far longer than ever anyone would wish to. He sang like a nightingale and pleased everyone. He pleasured all the women and lasses with his beard and his kisses and sent everyone mad with his frolics and fun and enjoyment in a way no mortal man could ever have done."

He paused for a breath and the Lords and the King again laughed heartily, but William had by no means finished.

"But all that was nothing," he went on. "I'm a plain man as you may see and who, looking at me, would say that a gaberlunzie could twist me round his little finger as easily as a piece of thread? Yet this beggar did just that. Your Majesty's men came to seize him and who ever saw William Hume of Cairnkibbie harbour or protect a thief? Yet we swore we would defend him even though we saw the stolen mace in his hand. And he had to do no more than whisper in our ears before the barn doors were shut and your men all locked up inside. Could any beggar of ordinary flesh and blood have have done all that, Your Majesty?"

William again paused for breath and again laughter resounded around the hall.

"But even that was little or nothing," added William. "For then, to repay all the good we had done him, he made himself invisible and rode off like the wind on the best horse there was about the place and since that moment no-one has seen hide nor hair of him."

"Are you satisfied, my Lord Ross?" demanded the King in a whisper to the baron sitting beside him. "Is our wager not won? Have we not succeeded? Dressed as a beggar, have we not gained the love of the members of the Maiden Feast so well as to make them rise in our defence against the King's knights and win the day?"

"I admit it," replied Lord Ross. "Your wager is indeed well and truly won."

"Stay where you are for the moment, William Hume,"

51

pronounced the King in tones of doom. "I will just go out and fetch my black cap before pronouncing sentence. To lay this crime on the devil is just the usual excuse of the wicked."

At the mention of the black cap Lilly screamed and Jean, her mother, cried for mercy while the farmer, thunderstruck, sat waiting his doom. The King retired and in a moment returned wearing on his head Wat Wilson's cap and carrying in his hand the stolen mace. Immediately the farmer recognised the identity of both the King and the beggar and all fears were at once dispelled.

"Stand up, Lilly Hume and Will Carr," cried the King.

The voice of royalty sounded ominous in the ears of the simple lass and she recalled how she had told the beggar the secret of her love and she blushed to the temples. She could scarcely stand without her father's supporting hand, but he, now seeing how the land lay, was not without hope that the services he had performed for the beggar king might be rewarded.

"So your father will not allow you to marry William Carr, Lilly, because he is poor," resumed James. "Is that not so?"

Lilly hung her head and William himself nearly blushed at his family secret coming out in the open in this way.

"Is this true, William Hume?" demanded the King, seeing he was never likely to get an answer from Lilly herself.

"I fear it is," agreed William. "But I would not have had it said because Will Carr is a decent man and his folk also, who cannot help their poverty, which is no fault of theirs."

"Do you now still stand by that as your objection to the match?" demanded the King.

"If your Majesty in the guise of Wat Wilson could command me and the whole household of Cairnkibbie to do your bidding," replied Will Hume with a smile, "I would have small chance of resisting your authority as King of Scotland. I have no objection to the match seeing that the King himself gives out the banns."

"William Hume," replied the King, laughing heartily. "Hear thy doom. For the love you did extend to our royal person we give you a free grant of the lands of Cairnkibbie upon this one condition: that you consent to the union of your daughter Lilly Hume and Will Carr, to whom, out of the royal purse, we shall give a marriage portion of 200 marks."

"I cannot disobey the commands of Wat Wilson," replied William Hume with a dry smile. "He has already exercised great authority over us all and we will not throw off our allegiance on this eventful day."

A general laugh finished the scene in court and the young couple went on to be married forthwith. The wedding feast was another great evening's celebration, and the old blind piper played his part merrily. The only person absent was the gaberlunzie who had been the life and soul of the Maiden Feast.

This story appears to have taken place near the hamlet of Foulden about ten miles south east of Duns, in east Berwickshire, although the farm of Cairnkibbie no longer exists.

Duns is today an attractive small town at the foot of the Lammermuirs. It makes a pleasant base for touring the Merse (i.e. the land in Berwickshire between the Lammermuirs and the Tweed), the Lammermuirs themselves and many attractive inland Border towns and villages such as Greenlaw and Kelso.

THE SURPRISE OF
FAST CASTLE

The first half of the sixteenth century in Scotland saw a number of unprovoked English invasions which bedevilled the latter part of James V's reign. In 1523, after offering his daughter Mary in marriage to the young James V and being refused, Henry VIII sent the Duke of Norfolk at the head of an army to invade Scotland. He burned and sacked both Jedburgh and Kelso and the surrounding area. In 1542, angered at James's continued alliance with France and his adherence to the old religion, Henry again sent the Duke of Norfolk and an army into Scotland, sacking and burning Jedburgh and Kelso and some twenty villages. In retaliation James sent a Scots army south in the same year. It was decisively defeated at Solway Moss and numerous leading Scots made prisoner, many of whom were subsequently freed on promising to support Henry's policies. James, always a mercurial character and already a sick man, took to his bed totally disheartened at the news of the defeat. A month later his French Queen, Mary of Guise, gave birth to a daughter, Mary, and within a week James had died.

Henry VIII then tried to secure the marriage of the infant Mary to his son Edward, who was to become Edward VI. Although this was agreed by a treaty of 1543 it was subsequently annulled by the Scots. Henry then embarked on his famous policy of "rough wooing", sending the Earl of Hertford to invade Scotland in 1544 and again in 1545; Edinburgh, Holyrood and Leith, Dryburgh, Melrose and Kelso were all sacked and burned, which, however, merely made the Scots more determined to resist.

In 1547, on Henry VIII's death, the same policy of "rough wooing" was continued by the Protector, Somerset, who invaded Scotland again. Although the Scots assembled a much larger army to repel the invaders they were over-confident and out-generalled. They were decisively defeated at the battle of Pinkie, just outside Musselburgh, and some 10,000 Scots were killed. The English then seized and fortified the town of Haddington and occupied most of the area south to Berwick.

Only by a last uneasy alliance with the French were the English, after some eighteen months, finally expelled. It is against this background that the following tale took place.

A LITTLE to the north of St Abb's Head, where the cliffs thrust forward into the North Sea in a distinctive manner known to countless fishermen and seafarers over the centuries, are the ruins of Fast Castle. Standing on its own pinnacle of rock, a giddy height above the waves which beat endlessly against its base, and surrounded by wheeling, crying seabirds, it is clear at first sight what an impregnable stronghold it must once have been. It is difficult to imagine how it could have been successfully stormed in the days before heavy artillery was available.

In 1547 the Duke of Somerset, acting as Protector during the minority of Edward VI, invaded Scotland and soon captured many of the important strongholds in the Borders, including Fast Castle, where he left a governor and a strong garrison. In the course of subjugating the district they forced the local people to take an oath of fealty to King Edward VI and renounce their allegiance to the young Queen Mary, who was still only a child. It was decreed by the English invaders, who were harrying the country from

Haddington as far as the gates of Edinburgh, that all the area from Berwick to Haddington was to be considered an English province, rightly part of England.

The English governor at Fast Castle commanded the local people to keep the garrison supplied with food from time to time. In accordance with the principle that the area was part of England, the people were treated as if they were subjects of Edward VI and not a people with whom the English were at war. They were thus paid with gold coin for the provisions they provided and payment was liberal for it was appreciated that some of the locals at least were only half-hearted in their allegiance to the Scottish crown. It was felt that such a policy might win more adherents than simply taking what they required at sword point. Nor was this without some effect, for there were admittedly a few who obeyed the edicts of the governor in Fast Castle willingly enough. There were others, however, who only did so because they knew well enough that to do otherwise was likely to cost them their lives.

At this time one of the well known inhabitants of Coldingham was a tall and powerful widow of around fifty named Madge Gordon. Every day she openly cursed the presence of the English and jeered at those who submitted to the English governor's commands. She herself had a score of poultry and a couple of cows but she vowed she would throw the eggs and the hens themselves over the cliffs and spill the milk over the ground rather than allow either to go to feed the English garrison at Fast Castle. Whenever she saw her neighbours carrying baskets over their arms, or sacks over their backs, or driving horses carrying provisions towards the castle she would vent her anger on them loudly.

"You're nothing more than slaves," she accused them on one occasion. "How long are you going to cringe before the hand that strikes at you, or kiss the foot that tramples on your country? Throw that food away and feed them on the points of your fathers' swords instead. That's what they deserve!"

Some of them attempted to laugh at her remarks but most felt the truth of her words deep in their hearts.

"You're just plain daft, Madge," one replied, with an uneasy grin. "But the governor's not likely to take any notice of a gabby woman's tongue so you're safe enough!"

"What do I care for him, you spiritless oaf," replied Madge fiercely. "Go and tell him Madge Gordon defies him and his men to do their worst, just as she despises you for crawling to him. If you had a drop of the blood of the men who bled with Wallace and with Bruce in your veins, the flag of Scotland would wave over the towers of Fast Castle before sunset!"

"Mother! Mother!" cried her daughter Janet, a good-looking lass of about nineteen, who had come to the door of the house at the sound of her mother's voice raised in anger. "Don't talk so foolishly, or you'll be getting us into trouble!"

"Trouble, you foolish lass!" cried Madge. "These are indeed times to talk of being in trouble, when our wretched country is groaning beneath the yoke of the enemy and we can see them harrying us out of house and home and destroying our men's very manhood."

"Look over there!" she added, pointing across the road. "Do you see who that is, skulking as far as he can get from our door with a well-filled sack on his shoulders? It's your own dear John Wilson, betraying his country. He's a coward, Janet, like the rest of them and he'll not call you his wife while I live to call you daughter!"

"Oh, mother!" replied the lass in upset tones. "What could poor John do? It isn't as easy for a man as it is for us. If he didn't do as everyone else does he'd be informed against and so he has to obey the orders or die."

"Let him die, then, as a man and Scotsman!" replied Madge Gordon firmly.

John Wilson, who had for some time been Janet's betrothed, was a young man of twenty-three who held, as his forefathers had done before him, sheep lands under the house of Home. It was only the invasion of the countryside which had prevented him from marrying Janet earlier. He was one of those who only reluctantly obeyed the edicts of the governor of Fast Castle to provide food for the garrison. Until the day Madge caught sight of him with the sack on his shoulders he had refused to do so. Turncoats, however, had passed word of his stubbornness to the governor and to save himself from retribution he had decided to take some token corn to the castle.

He was well aware of his prospective mother-in-law's fierce patriotism, which was why, as Madge had noticed, he had tried to avoid being seen passing their door while carrying provisions for the enemy. That evening, when he paid his regular evening visit to Janet, Madge accosted him at once in the doorway.

"Out! Out! You traitor!" she cried. "The shadow of a coward shall never cross our door while I have a hand to prevent it."

"I am no coward!" John replied indignantly.

"What are you then?" she demanded. "Did I not see you with my own eyes, this very day, carrying meal to the enemy?"

"You might have done," replied John. "But one man cannot take a castle, or drive five hundred enemy troops from it. Just wait a while. Foolhardiness is not the same as courage. If more prudence and caution and less over-confidence had been shown by our army last year we would not today have to mourn over losing the battle of Pinkie. I tell you again therefore, just wait a little."

"Come you in, John," said Madge in changed tones. "Draw up a chair and sit you down. Now tell me what you mean?"

"Now then, John!" said Janet in tones of reproach and alarm. "Are you going to be as harebrained as mother? What does it matter to us who's king, or who's queen? It will be long enough before either of them does anything for us. When you see lords and the gentry accepting English money and taking the English side, what can the likes of you or mother do?"

58

"What can we do, you chicken-hearted lassie, fearful of your own shadow?" interrupted Madge. "Though I may be somewhat past my prime I've still got an arm that's strong and healthy and the blood that runs in it is as good as the finest of them."

Madge's maiden name was Home and when her pride was touched it was her habit to run through her father's family tree back to that George, fourth Earl of Home, who had fallen while fighting against Somerset's invasion only a few months earlier. She would then continue back for a further six hundred years, ending up in a fine glow of offended aristocratic pride.

"What can the likes of your mother do?" she concluded warmly. "Now talk of the likes of your mother!"

"Ah, well, mother," replied Janet mildly. "All that may be true enough, but there's no need for you to fly into a tantrum over my words, for I meant nothing by it. It's just that I don't want John putting his life at risk to no purpose. I just wish our nobility would keep their side of the bargain and allow our Queen, though she may be just a child, to be married to young King Edward. Then we might have some peace in the land and other folk could be married the same as them."

"We shall be married, Janet my love," replied John, gazing at her ardently. "Only just wait a little while."

"Tell me, John," asked Madge. "What do you mean by a little while? Have any of you made a plan and are you now waiting to put it into action, is that it?"

"No," he replied frankly. "I cannot say that we've any useful plan as yet, but there are hundreds of us ready to draw our swords and strike when the slightest chance of success offers itself. And the chance will come, of that I'm sure!"

"And amongst these hundreds of folk you speak of," asked Madge, "is there not one who has suggested a plan to overpower the enemy and recapture Fast Castle?"

"I don't think anyone has thought of a sound plan yet," admitted John sadly. "At least if they have I have not heard of it yet."

Madge sat thoughtfully with her chin in her hand for some minutes. Then at last she stirred herself.

"When do you next intend to go back to Fast Castle to sell them provisions?" she enquired.

"This day next week," John replied.

"Then in that case I'll take my basket and some eggs and butter and go with you," she replied.

"Oh, mother, you can't mean it! What are you saying?" cried Janet. "You must not do anything of the kind. I know you and your temper would flare up the moment you heard a word spoken against Scotland and then there's no telling what might happen."

"Leave both my actions and their consequences to me, Janet my lass," replied her mother. "As I brew so I will drink. But you need have nothing to fear. I will be as quiet in the castle as you would be giving John your hand in the kirk."

On the appointed day the following week, when everyone gathered to carry provisions to Fast Castle, to the general surprise Madge appeared with a basket on each arm and mingled amongst the crowd. There was a good deal of comment freely bandied about.

"Oh aye, so Madge likes to turn a penny as well as other folk," said some.

"The English will do well if they get any sort of a bargain from her baskets and then it'll likely choke them," said the more discerning.

She duly went with them to the castle carrying her eggs and milk like the rest of the populace. Under pretence of disposing of her goods to the best advantage she made a thorough tour of inspection of the castle and did not leave until she had learned how it was guarded and which were the strong and which the weaker points of its defences.

When John came to her house that evening on his usual visit to Janet, Madge was ready for him.

"Now, John," she said. "I have seen our enemies and their strengths and weaknesses. And I have something to say that will test your courage and that of the hundreds of good men you say are just waiting their time to strike. Now is it your opinion that between Dunglass and Eyemouth you could raise a hundred men willing and ready to draw their swords for Scotland to drive the invaders from Fast Castle if a feasible plan could be put before them?"

"I have no doubt of it!" he replied.

"Doubts will not do," she replied. "Will you try it?"

"Yes," he replied stoutly.

"John, you *shall* be my son," she replied, taking his hand. "I see there is spirit in you."

"Mother," cried Janet anxiously. "What dangerous task is this you would set him on? What do you think it matters to me who is governor of Fast Castle if John should meet his death in the attempt?"

"Quiet, lassie!" replied her mother. " Had I not borne you I would say you had not a drop of my blood in your veins. What is it you fear? If they follow my plan, although it may try their courage, we'll accomplish the task with little harm to our side."

"Do not fret or fear, my love," said John. "I have a hand to defend my head and a good sword to guard both." Turning to Madge he continued: "What is your plan so that I can pass it on to those I know to be faithful to our cause?"

"If I were to tell you now," she replied scathingly, "and you were to let them know before we were ready to put it into effect, the story would spread from Tweedside to John O'Groats and from St Abbs to the Solway. We'd have the English on our necks before we could move. No, my lad, my scheme must be laid before all the true men that can be gathered together at the same time and within a few hours of being put into execution. You know that dark copse above Houndswood, where there is a narrow opening through the trees leading to a fine patch of meadowland where a thousand men might camp unseen?"

"I do," replied John thoughtfully.

"And do you think you could assemble the hundred good men and true that you speak of there this day fortnight?" she demanded.

61

"I will try," replied John earnestly.

"Try your best," she commanded him. "And I will meet you there before the moon sinks behind the Lammermoors."

A few days after this meeting Madge was summoned to the village of Home to attend the funeral of a relative. While she was there the castle of her ancestors was daringly seized from the control of Somerset's troops by an aged kinsman of hers along with a handful of armed men. This courageous action fired her own ardour more strongly than ever and renewed her resolve to wrest Fast Castle from the English, come what might.

She remained at Home until the day she was due to meet John Wilson and his hundred stout-hearted and trusty men at the meadow above Houndswood. She then went straight to the meeting place without returning home. As she approached the narrow opening to the meadow the young moon was already beginning to sink behind the Lammermoor hills. When she drew cautiously nearer she could hear the buzz of voices gradually becoming audible.

"Well, John, what are you waiting for?" someone was saying. "What's this grand project you wanted to lay before us?"

"Yes, John, let's get down to business," said another. "It will be dark soon and I have to get back to Pease Bay tonight."

"Have patience," John answered. "Just wait a little longer."

"What for, man, what for?" demanded another impatiently.

"She said she'd be here before the moon went down behind the Lammermoors," John began to reply hesitantly.

"Who do you mean? Who promised to be here?" enquired the questioner persistently.

"I did!" replied Madge, proudly, stepping out of the narrow entrance into the meadow in the fading light of the moon. With a regal bearing she strode into the midst of them, a tall and stately figure, as if all the blood and dignity of the Homes had been centred in her frame.

"Well, Madge," the same man continued. "Since you've come, perhaps you'll tell us why we're here?"

"To see, as you have inherited your fathers' blood, whether you have also inherited their spirit. To see whether you have the manhood to break the chains of the oppressors and the courage to follow the example set by the men of Home the other night."

"What did they do?" enquired John.

"Listen to me," she replied, "and I will tell you. You all know that for nearly two years the English have held Home Castle, just as they still hold Fast Castle. Well, it was just the other night and just as the gloaming was darkening the towers of Home that an old kinsman of mine scaled the walls of the castle where they were highest, strongest and least guarded. Thirty gallant countrymen had gone with him, but before they could follow him he was seen by a sentry, who shouted the alarm, 'To Arms! To Arms!' But my old kinsman had time to descend the walls again and warn his men to hide in the whin bushes at the foot of the walls. There he joined them and they lay with their swords drawn but well concealed from the battlements.

"There was running and clanking and shouting throughout the castle for a while, but as nothing like the presence of any enemy could be seen and there were no traces of anyone about, the sentry who had raised the alarm was laughed at. Some of the men went back to bed and others back to their wine. Then gradually all was quiet again and two hours later my old kinsman led the way once more with his followers behind him. Bursting into the castle they shouted, 'Hurrah for Scotland and Home for ever!' The garrison were seized with panic and within ten minutes every man-jack was put to the sword or surrendered. And now, neighbours, what my old kinsman and a handful of countrymen did for the deliverance of Home Castle can we not also do for Fast Castle and so drive the invaders out of Berwickshire?"

"Well, Madge, that's all very well," replied one of the men who appeared to be the most influential amongst them. "I don't mean to say that your kinsman and his men did not perform a very gallant act and I would be glad to do the same at Fast Castle tonight, but the thing is impossible. There's no comparison. At Fast Castle with the drawbridge up there's that dark deep chasm between you and eternity. I say again it's impossible. Who has the head to look down from the dizzy heights of Wolf's Crag let alone think of climbing it? I would have been willing enough to tackle any practicable plan but it would be madness just to throw away our lives without the slightest chance of success."

"Listen to me," replied Madge. "I know just as well as you what's possible and what's impossible. But if your hearts beat as stoutly as your fathers did, Fast Castle can be ours and the invaders driven out before this hour on the morrow. You will not have forgotten that tomorrow we have been ordered to take provisions to the garrison. I shall be with you and in the lead. But although my left hand will be holding a basket, my right hand will be holding under my cloak the sword my husband bore in the wars against King Henry. When I reach the last sentry I shall cry, 'Now, lads, now! For Scotland and our Queen!', and who dare follow my example?"

"I dare! I will!" replied John Wilson at once. "In the morning every man of us will enter the castle with arms concealed about him and have them ready to draw and strike at a moment's warning. My friends, you cannot say, but that this is a feasible plan and you'll not be outdone in bravery by a woman surely? Do you agree to it?"

There were enthusiastic cries of assent all round. "Yes, John, Yes! Every man of us! That's an excellent plan and better late than never!"

"Gather round me then," said Madge sternly and they formed a circle round her. "Will you all swear in the presence of Him who sees through the darkness of the night and searches the individual heart that none of you will betray to the English what we have decided on this night but that every man of you in the morning will do your utmost even at the price of your life to deliver our country from the yoke of our oppressors? Do you swear?"

"We swear!" they replied with bowed heads as one man.

"Away with you then," she replied. "Each man to his own home and get your weapons ready."

Leaving the meadows they each took their own paths back across the moors to their homes. Madge herself returned to her home accompanied by John. When they entered the house it was to find Janet anxious and at her wit's end because she had expected her mother to return two days previously. When she saw her in John's company she at once guessed that her formidable mother had prevailed on him to undertake some dangerous course of action and she then at once became anxious on his behalf.

When he rose to leave she went with him to the door.

"John, my dear," she said fondly. "You and my mother are up to something, I am sure. You have some secret you will not tell me. What is it?"

"The only secret between us," he replied, "is that she consents that if you are willing tomorrow you shall be my bride – if you so wish, as I am sure you do! But I did not wish to put you out by mentioning that in front of her."

Janet blushed, but went on determinedly. "But there is something more than that between you, John, and why should you hide it from me?"

"Dearest," he replied, "I cannot imagine why you are so apprehensive. There's nothing between your mother and me that is not well known by everyone in the country. But just have patience. Wait a little longer, only until tomorrow morning and when I come to lead you to the minister I will tell you everything then."

"And why will you not tell me now, John?" she demanded. "I am sure there is something brewing between you and something dangerous at that! Do you not trust me? You may think me a weak sort of woman and I may not be as boldly outspoken as my mother, but just try and see if I have not a stout enough heart when it's needed."

"Well, Janet my love," replied John, "I'll not deny there's something brewing, but what it is I am not at liberty to tell anyone. I am bound by an oath not to speak of it and so are a hundred others as well as me. But in the morning it will be in my power to tell you all. Now just be content and get ready for our wedding."

"But my mother knows . . . ," began Janet, when her mother's voice was raised from the house.

"Come in now, Janet," she cried. "What are you waiting for out there in the cold? You've been long enough with John tonight. Tomorrow night you may speak with him as long as you like. So come away in, lassie."

Madge was not a parent whose children were likely to require telling twice. With a last fond "goodnight" to her John, Janet returned to the cottage and her bed.

It was not long after sunrise next morning when a gathering of over a hundred of the local populace appeared at the castle laden with provisions as the governor had commanded. There were fishermen from Eyemouth and Coldingham, shepherds from the hills above Dunglass with slaughtered sheep, millers and small farmers from the edges of Coldingham moor with oats and vegetables. Accompanying them also were a few women carrying butter, eggs and milk, cheese and poultry.

The narrowness of the drawbridge over the deep chasm, beyond which the castle stood on its pinnacle of rock, caused the visitors to form a long procession as they entered the castle walls. In the lead was Madge Gordon accompanied by her son-in-law-to-be John Wilson. The drawbridge had been let down. The last of the procession had crossed over it and Madge had reached the furthest sentry. Then, suddenly dropping her basket, she drew her dead husband's gleaming sword from under her grey cloak.

"Now, lads, now!" she cried. "For Scotland and our Queen!"

As she spoke she buried the sword up to the hilt in the sentry nearest her. At her cry every man threw aside his burden and a hundred hidden swords were drawn. In a few minutes every sentry was overpowered.

"Forward lads! Forward" shouted Madge, pressing forward into the castle itself.

"Forward!" cried John Wilson leading the way with her, sword in hand.

They surged on into the castle and there divided themselves up into bands. Some took charge of the arsenal where the arms were kept. Others rushed from room to room securing those of the garrison who surrendered readily and showing no quarter to those who resisted. Within half an hour Fast Castle was in their hands and the entire garrison had either fled, been slain or were prisoners.

Besides striking the first blow Madge had not let her husband's sword remain idle during the fight. As the victors gathered round John Wilson to acknowledge that they owed their victory to his counsel, presence of mind, leadership and courage, Madge pressed forward. Presenting him with her still bloody sword she cried:

"Take this, my son, and keep it! It was the sword of a brave man and it goes to a brave man. Tonight you shall be my son indeed!"

"Thank you, Mother!" replied John Wilson and as he spoke a faint smile crossed his lips.

Hardly had he taken the sword in his hand than Janet's voice was heard.

"Where is he?" she shouted. "Where's my mother? Where is my John? Does he still live?"

"Here, love! Here. It's my Janet," John cried, but his voice seemed to fail him as he spoke.

"Come, my daughter!" said her mother. "And in the presence of these witnesses receive a hand you may be proud of."

As the remainder of the defeated garrison had fled through Coldingham Janet had learned of the surprise by which the castle had been captured and immediately knew the secret her betrothed had refused to tell her. She then at once ran to the castle to learn what had happened to them.

As she rushed forward the crowd round John Wilson stepped back. He went forward to greet her but he was seen to stagger as he moved. When Janet fell on his breast and her mother clasped their hands together the crowd gave a loud cheer at the sight.

He spoke but one word. "Janet!" he cried as he clasped her to him, then his arms fell away and he fell backwards to the ground.

"John! John!" shrieked Janet. "He is wounded! Help him!"

Madge and some of the spectators tried to raise him, but his eyes were closed and he could only mutter, "Water! Water!"

He had been wounded in the thick of the action, but had not realised then that it was a mortal blow. They carried him into the castle, but before he could be laid decently down on a bed he had died. The wretched Janet clung to his body and murmured loving words.

"John, my John, we shall be married tonight!" she cried frantically, and then she turned on her mother accusing her of murdering her John.

Finally those present were forced to lift her from his body and tried to calm her. Her mother Madge stood as if she had been struck with a palsy in the moment of her triumph.

"My poor bereaved child," she cried, taking her daughter in her arms and embracing her lovingly. "You have indeed cause to mourn for John was a noble lad, but oh, do not say it was my doing, lass. Do not blame your mother! It is surely some comfort that John has died for Scotland like a hero!"

But Janet never recovered. Her spirit was completely broken from that day and, although her mother did her best to look after her and help her, she remained inconsolable and within two years she was laid to rest beside John Wilson in Coldingham kirkyard. Before another winter had passed the brave spirit of Madge Gordon lay at rest alongside them.

The ruins of Fast Castle on its pinnacle of rock remain today an impressive spectacle a little over three miles north of St Abb's Head, best approached from the Coldingham road and by a short walk over the fields to the cliff top. The incessant cries of the gulls and crash of waves at the base of the Wolf's Crag add to the impressiveness of these remains, but care is advised with children or dogs, or anyone subject to vertigo.

Eyemouth, an atttractive small fishing port, once a smuggling centre, about three miles south of St Abb's Head makes a pleasant base from which to visit this part of the coastline. Alternatively, Coldingham itself is an attractive little village with plenty of accommodation. Further north, the coastal holiday resort of Dunbar makes a good base from which to tour this part of Berwickshire and East Lothian and as far afield as Haddington or Edinburgh.

East Lothian has three noteworthy castle ruins worth visiting, all rather better preserved than Fast Castle: Dirleton Castle, sited in the village of Dirleton; Tantallon Castle, a spectacularly sited and impressive ruin close to the popular coastal resort of North Berwick and facing the Bass Rock; and Hailes Castle, near East Linton, pleasantly placed beside the river Tyne.

HARDEN'S REVENGE

During Mary's reign, despite the religious troubles in Scotland following the Reformation, there were no further major invasions. The English and Scots in the Borders were learning to live at peace with each other, due in part to the system evolved over the centuries of regular meetings between the Wardens of the Marches on either side. These posts were generally filled by members of prominent families in the regions recognised as the West, Middle and East Marches. At the regular quarter days they met informally to give judgment on the complaints by either side. Where there had been some obvious wrong committed on either side it could be redressed by the mutually agreed judgment of the Wardens.

Such meetings, although only providing a rough and ready form of justice, did at least help to keep the peace. Sometimes, however, when the truce at such meetings was broken, they could turn into a scene of bloodshed, as at the Reisdswire in 1575, which was nearly the cause of full-scale war. The Scottish Warden of the Middle March was Sir John Carmichael, who owed his appointment to being a favourite of the Regent, the Earl of Morton. His English opposite number, Sir John Forster, member of a prominent Border family, probably regarded him with contempt.

A decision was queried. The English Warden made some derogatory comments. The English attacked and the affair developed into a full-scale battle. The English, at first successful, were roundly defeated by the arrival of Scottish reinforcements from Jedburgh. The danger of it developing further was avoided only by some diplomatic moves by Morton and Elizabeth.

By the recognised Border Law, known as the "Hot Trod", a cattle raider might be pursued even over the Border if necessary, "with hue and cry, with horse and hound". If, however, he retained the stolen cattle for a week and a day without being detected and denounced, they automatically became his property. From the foregoing it will be appreciated that the "Border Law" was very close to a form of legalised anarchy. On the other hand, recognition of the advantages of the legal process on occasions was slowly becoming more widespread.

WALTER, OR Wat, Scott of Harden, also known in the Border way simply as Harden, or even Wat Harden, after the name of his property, lived in the latter half of the fifteenth century during the period when Border reiving was possibly at its worst. He lived in the ancient family seat, Harden Castle, a fortress of considerable strength standing on the edge of a precipitous cleft not far from the river Borthwick. Below was a dark and steep-sided glen bounded by a burn which ran into the main river. The situation was well sited both for the castle and its owner, providing an impregnable stronghold for his defence while the glen made an excellent paddock, known as 'the Beef Tub', for the cattle he had obtained by the old custom of reiving, or rustling, from his neighbours, whether Scots or English.

Wat Harden's fame had spread far and wide throughout the Borders for, like the fabled young Lochinvar, he was gallant both in love and war. It was also entirely true that he never looked at an article of man's making, or nature's production, without considering whether it was moveable or a fixture. When a young man he had courted and wed the "Flower of Yarrow" as she was known, Mary Scott, the daughter of Philip Scott of Dryhope. It says much for his father-in-law's understanding of his prospective son-in-law that in the marriage contract he stipulated that, in return for the proceeds of "the first moonlit night", he would "find Harden in horse meat and man's meat at his tower of Dryhope for a year and a day", but that at the expiry of that period, his son-in-law should remove himself, *without attempting to continue in possession by force"*.

It was said that the only period of Wat Harden's entire life when his unusual moral attitude towards other people's property was not being actively pursued was during the first month of his marriage to Mary Scott in 1576. During that lunar month the "Flower of Yarrow" occupied his attention fully. Apart from that short period, however, he was on horseback almost every moonlit night wreaking mayhem amongst his neighbours' cattle or sheep if they were unwise enough to leave them unprotected.

Mary Scott, although the fairest lass in the Borders in her day, took just the same delight in cooking other people's cattle or sheep as her husband had in returning home with them. She had the familiar Border wife's habit when meat was short of mentioning to a retainer in her husband's hearing that "Harden's cow was looking lean", or else presenting him at the table with a pair of freshly polished, gleaming steel spurs in an empty pie dish as a broad hint that it was time he was up and about his business of securing fresh supplies for the household.

During the first six years of their marriage she also presented him with six fine sons, who in course of time grew up to be young men, well versed by their father in his particular way of life. It was their father's ambition, however, to see each son settled as an independent proprietor on a property where he might operate on his own account in later years. He already had obtained four good properties intended for the inheritance of four of his sons. Two remained to be provided for and here one great problem faced him. By this time the practice had already been introduced of regulating the rights to land by charters on pieces of parchment, whereby the outside of a sheep, itself a very readily conveyable beast, was made to vest a right in the land on which it had grazed.

He particularly wished to obtain the estate of his neighbour, William Scott of Gilmanscleugh. He had often ridden over the ground on his many forays abroad both in moonlight and during the day and knew it well. It was, he decided, perfect for one of his sons, but there was a major drawback in that, by an unfortunate coincidence of tastes, the two families had remained on a more or less friendly footing. The only solution appeared to be somehow or other to fall out with William Scott of Gilmanscleugh so that he would be able to claim his lands and obtain a grant to them.

In this situation Wat Harden sought his wife's advice, for she had often been helpful when planning raids or such diversions, and he knew from experience she could often devise a better plan than himself or anyone else he knew. On this particular question she was also in favour of securing Gilmanscleugh if at all possible.

"By my faith, Mary," said Walter. "If Gilmanscleugh had only four legs on it, it would not long remain the property of Will Scott."

"And if my Walter had the strength he once had, it would also soon enough be Harden's," she replied tartly. "My charms must have faded indeed. If the Flower of Yarrow had once asked her husband for Gilmanscleugh it would have been hers by the next morning. But it seems the years bring fears."

"Not to Harden, Mary, my love," replied Wat proudly. "He knows not the meaning of fear. Your dish of spurs makes me as ready to go as when the cook was the fairest maid in Yarrow. It's these accursed sheepskin rights, lass, that stop me gaining Gilmanscleugh for one of the lads."

"She who cooks the spurs, Wat, needs a fire," she replied stubbornly. "Charters will burn. I'll give you the spurs if you'll give me the parchment. It will help to roast one of Gilmanscleugh's beasts."

"But there may well be copies, Mary," Wat pointed out shrewdly. "What if there's more than one sheepskin?"

73

"Well, my fire's large enough," she replied stubbornly. "I've known you return with fivescore sheep in a night and the devil's in it if you cannot return with two sheepskins."

"For sure you are the Flower of the Yarrow reivers, Mary," Wat Scott replied with a smile. "Well, then, tell me where we will find a property for our other son?"

"Gilmanscleugh may serve them both," she replied.

"The woman's mad," he declared. "It's not enough for one of them, let alone two. If necessary Dryhope will have to be the answer for the youngest, despite my pledge to your father."

He might have said more but after an energetic day's hunting he was tired and in the mood for his bed, where he retired muttering to himself that even if he were to get Gilmanscleugh there was no way it could suffice for two sons.

In the morning he woke, still mindful of her words, and on arriving in the dining hall for his breakfast he found his wife and his six sons together in a group and from their furtive manner he at once suspected some plot between them. His wife Mary, however, was now engaged in her favourite occupation, namely feeding her gallant husband and six brave sons, the like of whom she was convinced were not to be found for looks and manhood in the whole of Scotland.

The family sat down and when the chief took the cover off the nearest dish there was loud laughter from them all, in which he himself joined, for his wife had made good her words of the previous evening and he found beneath it a pair of gleaming steel spurs.

"And towards what game are these spurs to send us, Mary, my dear Flower of Yarrow?" he asked good-humouredly.

"A good portion for our youngest," she replied. "The broad acres of Gilmanscleugh and all the beasts on it and especially the chest that holds the parchment, which will be given to me for safekeeping."

"And why not for our two youngest?" asked Harden a shade bitterly, despite his good humour. "Did you not say Gilmanscleugh might serve both of our remaining sons?

74

What right have the sons of the Flower of Yarrow to more than half of what suited one Scott of Gilmanscleugh? By my faith, Mary, were it not that I have such a good breakfast before me I might even quarrel with my Flower for demeaning the honour of Harden in this way. And if it were not for that confounded contract your father wheedled me into signing I'd seize Dryhope yet."

"Before we quarrel about its portions," she replied, "had we not better measure the size of Gilmanscleugh first?"

"I have driven too many of his cattle over his own ground and into Harden's Beef Tub not to know the breadth of it well enough," he replied. "But never mind, my lads, we will go over it today and get a good measure of its size. Harden never reives by day, but the light of the sun shows us more clearly what the moon may light us to by night."

After breakfasting on more substantial fare than the dish of spurs, they made their preparations for exploring Gilmanscleugh and examining his cattle and sheep, with a view to possibly inciting Will Scott into taking action and precipitating a quarrel. As a cover for these proceedings they prepared as if for a hunting expedition, after first taking a stirrup cup at the hands of the Flower of Yarrow. Then, mounted on their shaggy garrons, with bows slung over their shoulders and their swords by their sides, with two wolf-hounds of great size and strength and a number of baying stag-hounds rousing the echoes in the glen in harmony with their own hunting horns, they set off in the sort of group ready for the spoils of war or the hunt, of reiving or sport.

The mother of six manly sons and wife of the old bear of a husband had a natural proud light in her blue eyes as she watched them about to depart and gazed on one well-loved face after another.

"It was out hunting I first saw you, Walter, from the top of Dryhope Tower," she said. "And he who hunted then for a wife may well hunt now for a property for her sons."

"If I bring back Gilmanscleugh," Wat laughed at her, "it will be a larger quarry than the Flower of Yarrow!"

75

"You did not think so then, Wat," she replied, laughing back at him. "But perhaps love yields to ambition. The day you can call Gilmanscleugh your own, I will have to put your once so highly cherished Flower of Yarrow forward in competition. You will be a brave man, I can tell you, to prefer the new love to the old."

"I would not part with you, my good woman," he replied, "for all of Lauderdale with Ettrick Forest thrown in. So hold your peace and get on with your housekeeping, for we will be coming home hungry men."

He sounded his horn as he spoke and the signal was enough for them to set off at full speed down the hill and through the glen with all the impetuous swiftness of true Borderers, learned through years of speeding off with their stolen cattle to foil any rescue attempt. They were soon out of sight, but the sound of their horns and the baying of their hounds echoed and re-echoed off the distant hills and was music to the ears of the proud mother and wife remaining behind.

A true Borderer's wife of the period, she never worried about the possible dangers of any expeditions, whether hunting or fighting. Such was her own heroic spirit that much as she loved all her men she would have remained stoical and calm over the return of the dead body of any one of them and would have comforted herself with the thought that they had died nobly, in the way they had wished to live. The wives of the Borderers were remarkable for this ability to applaud the deeds of their husbands and sons and for the fortitude with which they bore the often tragic results of their actions.

At that moment Mary Scott, the Flower of Yarrow, thought only of the broad acres of Gilmanscleugh which she considered perfectly suitable for her two remaining sons who still required property. She already saw in her mind's eye the flame which would consume the parchment rights. In the same flames she planned to roast an ox to celebrate this fresh acquisition for the lands of Harden.

In the meantime the hunting party had spread out

through the woods, sounding their horns but caring less about the deer on their land so much as the cattle of Gilmanscleugh they knew awaited them. They were still on Harden's land when they heard the sound of another hunting horn in the distance. At once Harden sent off his youngest son, who was known as the Forester from his love of woodcraft, to gallop forward on his garron to see who had the temerity to hunt so close to Harden's land.

The young man, who was one of the sons as yet unprovided for, heard the horn ahead of him on the boundaries of Harden land and concluded that it was very probably Will Scott of Gilmanscleugh himself who was out hunting. It then struck him that by fastening a quarrel on him and getting quit of him with a swift sword thrust he would thus complete his parents' scheme and make short work of the whole business. With these thoughts exciting his mind he spurred forward at full gallop, his fierce wolf-hound Grim bounding and baying alongside him with his tongue hanging out over his slavering blood-thirsty jaws.

He had kept up this pace for some time and was a considerable distance from the rest of the party when he saw Gilmanscleugh's dog, another wolf-hound, bounding away to the left, no doubt on the track of its master. The moment the dogs saw each other they closed and locked in mortal combat, making the forest resound with their snarling and growling. Gilmanscleugh, hearing the sound of the fight, returned to save his favourite hound from the jaws of Harden's more powerful beast, which was famed as being unbeatable by any animal. Coming upon them he struck the fierce beast a blow, but young Harden, coming upon him, at once abused him fiercely for striking his dog. The abuse was such that the insulted Gilmanscleugh laid his hand on his sword. In a moment Forester had drawn his and seconds later they were locked in combat. In a fatal moment or two the youthful and handsome son of Harden was lying lifeless and bleeding profusely in the turf.

"Ho for Gilmanscleugh," cried the older man as he

sheathed his bloody sword and saw at once his danger. "Now indeed every tree in Yarrow woods will rise up to avenge the death of young Harden."

"Wolf! Come, Wolf!" he cried, turning round. "We must away at once for home. Home, boy, home."

But his hound was firmly held in the jaws of the nearly victorious Grim and the sound of Harden's horns was approaching every moment. Leaping down from his horse, Gilmanscleugh stood above the fighting dogs and thrust his sword through the heart of Grim, releasing his own hound Wolf. The dog, seeing no life in his opponent, bounded away after his master as he hastily remounted and fled from the scene.

Unfortunately for Gilmanscleugh he had wasted too much time and the Hardens were close upon him. The twang of a bow announced that an arrow was on its way and looking down he saw his faithful hound roll over with the shaft of an arrow piercing its spine.

"There goes my King's evidence left behind!" he cursed as he thrust the spurs deeper into the sides of his horse. "Now Harden will know that Gilmanscleugh has killed his son. Let us get safe back as soon as we may, but after that who knows what may follow?"

Meanwhile Harden and his sons had seen Gilmanscleugh in flight and had fired the arrow which laid his hound dead, but they had not yet seen the body of the old chief's youngest and favourite son lying in the long grass. However, it was not long before it was discovered. The sight of the sword still grasped in his lifeless hand and the pools of blood, apparently enough for two, told their own tale. It was not necessary to feel for the heart which had stilled. The pale face of the corpse, still handsome even in death, was enough to betray at a glance that the lad was past return. The body of the dead Grim and his dead antagonist, which they all recognised as Gilmanscleugh's hound, also confirmed the identity of the killer of their son and brother.

The tear-filled eye of the father immediately flashed with fire. Each of the remaining five sons raised a cry for revenge. "Ho, for Gilmanscleugh, with sword and fire-faggot," they cried. With one accord they would have turned and headed for Gilmanscleugh intent on attacking that almost impregnable tower with their swords, completely forgetting that there were only five of them against the massed ranks of Gilmanscleugh's followers.

"Steady, my lads, steady," cried their father, standing over the body of his favourite son. "A hundred years would not cool our fire or our determination to be revenged but sudden revenge lacks the same fullness of satisfaction. Anyway, first we must take back the body of your brother to his own home for his mother to lay out. She will have time to think that but yesterday she said that Gilmanscleugh would satisfy both her sons. It is too true, for Gilmanscleugh has already satisfied one and before long he shall satisfy the other."

His sons, although full of desire for instant retaliation, saw the wisdom of the old man's counsel and the necessity of doing as he suggested. Wrapping their brother's corpse in a cloak they started their sad journey back to Harden with it laid over the back of his garron. Thus it was that Mary Scott saw them returning. The slow and sad procession told its own grim story as soon as she laid her eyes on it.

She was not one to give way to paroxysms of grief at the sight of her favourite son lying dead. She saw Harden wipe away a tear from his eyes as he approached and she heard the sobs of Forester's brothers as they came near. Yet she approached them in the doorway with a firm step and stood to greet them without any outward show of emotion. When her husband met her he took her hand and motioned his sons to halt.

"Let them come in, Wat," she said steadily. "I know what it must be. My Forester is dead. Come forward, my sons, and tell me what cruel fate has been the cause of this."

The sons came forward carrying their brother's body between them and laid it inside the tower.

"Who has done this?" enquired the mother as she gazed at her son's pale face.

79

"Will Scott of Gilmanscleugh," replied Walter.

For the moment the sons' desire for revenge had been overcome by grief, but now at the mention of the name Gilmanscleugh it was like an electric shock on the brothers' minds. As one their hands moved to their swords and every face was turned to the door. But old Walter was watching them closely under his shaggy grey eyebrows and even as they turned to rush out seeking some sort of wild revenge he called them back.

"Let us plan this now, my bold lads," he said. "We must make a plan before rushing into action."

He led them to the small barred side room where the title-deeds for Harden and sundry valuable family treasures were stored for security. There he ushered them in ahead of him. As the last one entered he slammed the door shut and turned the key, removing it and placing it in his pocket.

"Now, give me the Forester's bloody doublet," he commanded his wife, "with the hole in the right breast made by Gilmanscleugh's sword."

"What are you up to, Wat?" demanded Mary, as she lifted her gaze from the face of her dead son to witness these surprising actions. "Why are you locking up our sons when our dead son's blood calls for vengeance on Gilmanscleugh? And what do you want his bloody doublet for? It should be hung as a flag over the smoking ruins of Gilmanscleugh's tower. If you are not prepared to lead our sons in revenge then leave it to me, for woman as I am, I will do it."

"Do you not recall your own words, Mary?" replied Walter. "Did you not say that Gilmanscleugh would serve both our sons? The one lying there is satisfied indeed and by the power of revenge the other shall not be disappointed either. Come, give me the doublet and see that you feed our sons meat enough through the bars of the strong room so that they may keep their blood warm and their hearts glowing for three days. Let Forester lie there during that time, but turn his head towards Gilmanscleugh. Now, the doublet!"

Mary failed to understand what her husband was about, but she knew well that he generally acted with prudence and wisdom so she quickly removed the doublet, stained as it was with blood, and handed it to Walter. He took it from her and, holding it up to the light from the window, looked through the hole. With that strange mixture of humour and deep seriousness for which he was noted, he declared with a grim smile:

"Through this rent I see the lands of Gilmanscleugh with the Harden arms above the door."

With this enigmatic statement he rolled up the doublet and hurried outside to his horse, where he fastened it to his saddle. Then, mounting his steed, he clapped his spurs to its flanks and was away at a gallop over the hill.

Confused by her emotions and the speed of events, Mary had not had time to demand a full explanation from him, although it is questionable if the determined and crafty old chief would have told her much of his intentions. Returning to the room where her son's body lay, she sat watching his corpse until her husband should return. Meanwhile the murmurings of her sons grew louder from the strong room where they were immured.

"We shall not be balked of our revenge, mother," cried the youngest through the door. "The Forester's blood cries out more loudly than our father's voice. Call for the servants and have the door broken down that we may get at Gilmanscleugh!"

"I cannot disobey your father's instructions," she replied. "Even though my Forester's eyes seem fixed on me and demanding vengeance I cannot let you go. Three days you must remain there. Then your father will return with Forester's bloody doublet to hang on the point of your spears as you ride to revenge his death."

"Where has our father gone?" the impatient youth demanded.

"I do not know," she admitted. "But those were his commands. I am to wait by Forester's body for three days and feed you meanwhile through the bars of the strong room."

"We will not survive three days unavenged, mother," said another son. "We will take on ourselves the responsibility of our release. Send us a man to break down the door. For just think. Gilmanscleugh may take flight and the Forester's ghost may wander for many moons in Harden's glen upbraiding his brothers for not avenging his death."

"I cannot and will not disobey your father," she answered firmly.

"Then we will force our freedom, mother," cried a third son.

"Disobedient boy, do not speak so," she replied. "Wait the three days and nurse your fire. I am sure your father will require of you as much avenging anger as you have when you hear his horn sound again his return to Harden."

It was only with difficulty that Mary prevailed on her impetuous sons not to break out of their imprisonment. For the three days she sat by the side of her son's corpse and at mealtimes handed the food to her other sons through the bars of the strong room. Her days and nights were filled with mixed thoughts as she listened to the grumbles of her sons on the one hand and gazed at the face of her murdered son on the other.

Her thoughts were naturally very mixed. Harden's actions had been so very strange since his son's death. In the first place locking up his sons and preventing them from taking revenge was very unlike his normal conduct. His words as he had gazed through the hole in the Forester's doublet were more like the words of a madman than of a man who proposed to take revenge for his son's death. It occurred to her that possibly his mind had been unhinged by his son's death and these thoughts, combined with her own as she looked at her son's corpse and heard the mutterings of her other sons, naturally worked on her own mind through the three days she spent awaiting Harden's return.

As the evening of the third day came with no sign of Harden's return, the sons grew even more impatient, shouting that they intended to summon men to break down the doorway and take their own revenge if their father did not appear. When twelve midnight came and went, the sons announced their firm intentions of starting for Gilmanscleugh in the morning regardless. Their mother was afraid to let them hear the doubts she herself had regarding their father's state of mind.

While she was gloomily contemplating the future the sound of a horn reverberated through the hills.

"There's our father's horn!" cried the sons, fully roused at the sound, which Mary herself knew well.

She rose and, looking through the windows, saw Harden riding at full gallop towards the castle by the light of the moon. In a moment he had leaped from his horse and was before his wife again.

"To horse! To horse! Come, my sons!" he cried unbolting the door of the strongroom. "Now for Gilmanscleugh with the fire and sword of the Hardens' revenge!"

A loud shout inside the chamber announced the relief and anticipation which his sons felt at the prospect of at last being released on their foe and finally revenging their brother's death. The door was thrown open and they streamed outside to get their horses. The chief cast one last look at his dead son, hurried out into the courtyard where every retainer who could ride and carry weapons was awakened and summoned to join them with all haste.

Within a very short time, for all had been awaiting the summons, a large party had assembled and was ready to ride by the light of the moon. The castle walls rang with their war cries as they prepared for battle. They set off at a gallop and barely slackened pace until they were in full sight of Gilmanscleugh bathed in the bright moonlight.

Here his sons noted that their father took none of the usual precautions common in a night attack to prevent those being assailed from learning too soon of an approach. He slowed them down and gathered them together in a solid mass, it is true, but then he trotted them up, silently enough but deliberately and boldly, to rein up in front of the main gate of the tower of Gilmanscleugh where Will Scott over the past three days had been residing behind tightly barred doors with the growing belief that the death of the Forester had not been traced to him.

The whole party was now assembled in front of the tower and Harden sounded his horn long and loud. Will Scott, the owner of Gilmanscleugh, appeared at a turret window and asked the meaning of this call at such a late hour.

"I have a paper under the King's hand to read to you, Gilmanscleugh," replied Harden.

"We had better leave it till the morning," replied Gilmanscleugh. "Our lights are out in the tower. I will wait on you at your own time, but let it be in the light of the day."

"The moon is Harden's time," rejoined Walter. "If you will not let us in to read it, then I must read it to you here by the light of this torch we have brought with us for the purpose. You shall hear the words of His Majesty, the King. I am only the royal commissioner and must do my duty."

The torch was held up and Harden called forward one of his stewards and ordered him to read the royal charter which he put into his hands. The man obeyed and announced in loud tones that the King, for the love and favour he bore to Walter Scott of Harden had conveyed and settled upon him and his heirs the land, tower and appurtenances of Gilmanscleugh, which formerly belonged to William Scott but had fallen to the Crown by escheat in consequence of the constructive rebellion of the said William Scott in killing the son of Harden known by the name of the Forester. The charter gave, in addition, full power to the said Walter Scott of Harden to take immediate possession of the property and to adopt all necessary steps for ejecting the former proprietor and his family from the said property.

"You have heard the King's writ," cried Walter Scott in stern tones. "What sayest you to the royal authority? I come here peaceably to demand the possession of Gilmanscleugh. If you will consent to depart and give me the key of the tower I will pass my word of honour for the safety of you and your people within. If not, I will enforce the King's authority. You have a quarter of an hour to decide. I will wait."

The reading of the writ and this announcement caused enormous surprise on all sides, not only to the unhappy Gilmanscleugh who was to be deprived of his ancestral lands, but also Harden's sons, who seemed about to be deprived of their revenge. While Gilmanscleugh withdrew to consider the terms offered to him, Harden's sons crowded round him imploring him to retract his promise of safety to the murderer of their brother.

The old chief, who had already worked out all the advantages and disadvantages of the agreement, realised well how much better the property of Gilmanscleugh with its fertile acres which the King had given him in return for the life of his son was, compared with the sterile revenge of killing the perpetrator, which once done would be over. He replied calmly to them that he regarded gaining the lands as his revenge and a very good revenge at that. He added, however, that if Will Scott did not immediately agree with the conditions proposed they might then have their way with him and the entire household, to kill, burn or hang as they wished. This announcement raised the hopes of the bloodthirsty sons, who could not imagine that Will Scott would tamely comply with such ignominious conditions. However that, as Harden had expected, was what happened.

In a short while Will Scott appeared and announced that on condition that he and his household should be allowed to go forth free and unharmed he would hand over the keys of Gilmanscleugh. Walter Scott of Harden agreed at once and the entire household slowly trooped out, led by Will Scott's wife, with an infant in her arms and three children holding her skirts, all weeping fearfully as they passed through the fierce troops of warriors outside. Then followed a sick son carried on a stretcher by two retainers. Next came the laird's mother who was over eighty years of age and had borne seven sons since her arrival at Gilmanscleugh sixty years previously. Finally came Will Scott himself, carrying the key in his hand. At the sight of

85

him Harden's sons moved forward threateningly but in a moment a stern command from their father made them fall back. The keys were handed over in silence and the late laird of Gilmanscleugh followed his family into the moonlight countryside to find a lodging for the night from one of their dependants.

Walter Scott of Harden looked after him as he disappeared into the shadows.

"Revenge enough," he declared. "Revenge enough and to spare."

Then, taking possession of the tower, he left some men to guard it and returned to his wife still sitting by the side of her dead son. By the custom of the Borders he could not be buried until his death was avenged. Now she looked up as Harden entered and eyed him hopefully for signs that revenge had been achieved.

"Is there no vengeance, Walter?" she cried. "Is it thus that a Harden returns from the house of the murderer of his own son, with blade unbloodied and clothes unsullied with the miscreant's blood?"

"Whether, Mary," answered Harden, "would you accept a charter to the lands of Gilmanscleugh passing it to Harden and his heirs for ever, or the blood of its master as satisfaction for the death of our boy who lies there dead?"

"I would rather have the lands," she replied. "And let the murderer enjoy if he can the life that is spared to him. Our revenge is then doubled for while life may be painful to him the land will continue to yield us pleasure and profit in after years."

"Here then, you may see the charter to the lands of Gilmanscleugh," he cried, holding it out to her. "I received it from the King as satisfaction for the murder, and now we may indeed say, as you so strangely predicted, that Gilmanscleugh has served both our sons."

The next day the corpse of the Forester was buried and for many years afterwards the lands of Gilmanscleugh remained in the family under the name of Harden's revenge.

Harden Tower still stands, four miles west of Hawick, in Roxburghshire. With modern additions, it is now the home of Lord Polwarth and has some interesting examples of feudal art.

Hawick itself, although principally a textile centre, makes a useful base for touring the Middle March and through Jedburgh as far east as Otterburn and Hexham, or down through Langholm into Cumbria, both routes much favoured by the old reivers.

A WIFE OR THE GALLOWS

Although the events in the Tale only took place shortly after the death of Wat Scott of Harden, when his eldest son, William, or Will, Scott had just succeeded him, already a slow change in Border attitudes was beginning to take place. The same attitude of acceptance to lawlessness and reiving of cattle was no longer quite as apparent as it had been. During James VI's minority, however, there was continual conniving and plotting amongst the nobility and a general breakdown in law and order throughout Scotland. At this stage the Borderers themselves had perforce largely taken the law into their own hands in a form of rough and ready justice, even if the Wardens of the Marches still exercised their powers at their quarterly meetings and enforced an overall discipline of a sort.

TOWARDS THE latter end of the fifteenth century the young laird of Harden, William Scott, eldest son of the Wat Scott already mentioned, was as impetuous and courageous a young Borderer as ever lived. He was also handsome, rash and stubborn. His family for generations had been amongst the leaders of the Border reivers, living by raiding the English south of the border, viewing them as their natural enemy, yet at the same time sustaining similar raids and repelling them with the philosophy acquired by centuries of bloody battles. Nor did they always stop at merely raiding the English over the border, for many a long memory of slights or injuries had resulted in feuds sustained between near neighbours over the years, and quite frequently Scot raided Scot paying little heed to the laws of the land.

Just such a situation existed between the Scotts of Harden and the Murrays of Elibank close by in Ettrick Forest. Thus it was that when young William Scott of Harden had taken his fill of wine one October evening the thought came upon him to make a raid on his neighbour, the, to him, elderly knight, Sir Gideon Murray of Elibank. No sooner had the thought crossed his mind than he was on his feet and gathering as many men as could readily be summoned around him.

In a few moments he had launched into a stirring speech on the benefits of the old ways of life in the Borders, when the man who was prepared to ride by night and fight with his sword could maintain himself at the expense of his adversaries.

"Who is our natural foe?" he cried rhetorically. "None other than that old greybeard loon Sir Gideon Murray of Elibank. The Murrays all have well stocked farmsteads with good fat cattle in them. Who will ride with me this fine moonlit night to find themselves with a stock of cattle in their own byres in the morning?"

The response from his listeners, some twenty daring young men, was a rousing cheer, as might have been expected in response to such a rousing speech from their youthful leader on a subject on which all felt strongly. Scarcely sooner said than done. They were quickly mounted on light, active, sure-footed horses used to covering the moorland hills and boggy patches round the Forest of Ettrick. Each was armed with a sword and some carried the double-headed Jedhart axe or an occasional firelock. At a brisk pace they set off towards Elibank with high hearts and hopes, but the womenfolk watching them go from the doors of the cottages were not so light-hearted for they remembered the old saying:

"When Scott of Harden rides by night there will be swords drawn and blood let by morning."

By Will Scott's side rode his elderly kinsman and retainer Simon Scott, who, truth to tell, was far from eager for the fray. He had done his best quietly to dissuade his kinsman and leader from starting off on what seemed to him a hastily planned and wrong-headed expedition, but to no avail. Willy-nilly he had been forced to go along, for no Scott of Harden had ridden against a foe without a representative of his kinsman's family riding beside him and Simon Scott felt the ties of blood stronger than those of commonsense.

As dawn approached they arrived at the rich pastures of Murray of Elibank to find them, to their surprise, unguarded and with no sign of a Murray to be seen. As Will Scott had proposed, they quickly rounded up cattle and sheep by the hundreds into a vast herd, driving them off before them with the inbred dexterity of the Borderer. Laughing and joking, they were soon on their way with still not a soul to be seen and no opposition from anyone. Young Will Scott with his kinsman Simon by his side brought up the rear to guard against any attempt at rescue. In this fashion they set off for Harden, soon convinced they were well away from all signs of pursuit.

The young Laird of Harden was discussing with his follower Simon whether they should roast a bullock whole on their return by way of celebration. Simon, ever a man with an eye to the future, was arguing, not very successfully, that they could do well enough without this extravagance and that it was nothing more than a waste of their newly acquired meat supplies. Suddenly they heard the sound of a bloodhound giving tongue behind them. At the sound their men redoubled their efforts to keep the mixed herd of stolen beasts moving as fast as possible, urging them on with whips and blows.

The Laird of Elibank, Sir Gideon Murray, was well into middle age, with a face of iron and a will to match. His mouth was like a sabre gash in his bearded face and his eyes glowed like twin furnaces under thatched brows of grey hair. A man never known to give or ask for quarter, he was fierce, forceful and determined, never heard to forgive an insult or turn away from a foe. He was also father of two daughters who, sadly for them, took after their father in looks if not in disposition. Both were unmarried and the eldest was known far and wide as Muckle-mou'd, or Large-mouthed, Meg. This unfortunate nickname her own father had unthinkingly bestowed on first seeing her in her cradle, when he remarked, "What a muckle-mou!" – completely forgetting from which side of the family this notable trait was inherited.

Warned in advance of the rash young Laird of Harden's plans, he had deliberately set a trap for the Scotts. Thus it was that the raiders had found no one guarding the cattle and sheep, for a force of fifty Murrays were waiting in ambush just where the Scotts were likely to be held up by a narrow glen. The raiders' every movement had been watched and the Murrays were ready to strike.

Hardly had the small band of Scotts and their hard-pressed beasts reached the chosen spot, where they were necessarily stretched out and exposed with young Scott and Simon far in the rear, than the Murrays charged down on them. Spread out in ones and twos and greatly out-numbered, the Scotts did their best to fight their way to their chief, but he and Simon were already surrounded by odds of more than ten to one.

"Yield, you rash young fool," cried Sir Gideon. "Or you will be strung up from the nearest tree for the cattle thief you are."

"Never, while there's breath in my body will a Scott yield to a Murray," cried young Scott defiantly. "If you want to fight and leave your *handsome* daughters fatherless and some of your young men, who might have been their suitors out of pity, dead as well, so be it!"

"You young devil," snorted Sir Gideon. "You've sealed your fate now! You may say what you wish to my head but not a word against my wife or daughters. You'll regret that soon enough."

With that brief exchange the Murrays and Scotts joined in combat. Surrounded and outnumbered but fighting to the last, young William Scott had his horse killed under him and received a blow on the head which stretched him unconscious on the ground. His kinsman Simon Scott, fighting doggedly beside him, was soon also knocked senseless.

In a few minutes young Will Scott and his kinsman were roped hand and foot and their few remaining followers were in full retreat, while the victorious Murrays rounded up their straying beasts and prepared to return home with them in triumph. The two senseless captives were laid across two pack ponies like so much baggage and before they had fully recovered their senses were lodged in the dark dungeon at Elibank to rue their rash venture and wait their fate at the hands of Sir Gideon.

The laird himself had no intention of doing anything but hang them from the nearest convenient tree as he had earlier threatened, but his wife was a sensible woman and as mother of two daughters, both of them homely looking girls, if not as ugly as the Scotts cared to claim, had other ideas.

"What would you be intending to do with that handsome young Laird of Harden now that you have captured him and clapped him in your dungeon?" she enquired, knowing the answer full well.

For answer the laird led her to the window and, pointing to a handsome oak tree standing in the courtyard, announced firmly, "D'you see that fine branch standing out from the others? Tomorrow in the morning young Scott of Harden and his old kinsman will hang together side by side from yon branch, or I'm no Murray."

"Ah, just as I thought," she replied equally firmly. "Which was why I asked the question. Do you not see that you are acting cruelly and foolishly in this case? A little sober thought would soon make you change your mind."

"Madam," he answered in offended tones, "as to cruelty, when did a Scott of Harden show me or mine any mercy? As to foolishness, I can see no way in which I am acting foolishly and I beg you to make yourself plain."

"Here you are. Sir, you have two daughters to marry, who

though good-hearted are not widely regarded as handsome girls," she declared forthrightly. "And in your dungeon and in your power have you not a suitable husband available? Is it not cruel to them and foolish on your part not to offer him a choice?"

"Indeed, my dear," the laird replied enthusiastically. "For once in your life you've hit the nail on the head. There's more wisdom in that suggestion than I'd have given you credit for. Tomorrow the young sprout of Harden will have the choice of marrying Muckle-mou'd Meg or hanging from that branch alongside his old kinsman."

"Well," smiled his wife. "It would indeed be a pity to cut off the lad in the flower of his youth and there's not much doubt about the choice he'll take, so that's at least one of your daughters off our hands."

"I'd not be too sure of that," replied the laird frowning. "That young devil is both proud and brave and about as wrong-headed and stubborn as any you'll find in the Borders. It wouldn't suprise me if he demanded to be hanged. I know well which my choice would have been had I been in his shoes."

"Ah, well," replied his wife smiling to herself at the prospect of an imminent marriage in the family, "I can guess which your choice would have been easily enough."

"Oh, you can, can you?" demanded Sir Gideon, somewhat nettled by his wife's complacency. "Then just tell me which it would have been, the wife or the gallows?"

"Ah, come now, Gideon, you know well that, you'd choose a wife rather than be hanged," she replied, shaking her head at the foolishness of the question.

"Well, that's just where you're wrong," he snorted. "I'd rather have hung than marry a wife I'd never seen and I'd not be surprised if that's his choice too. But you'd better prepare the girl for a wedding and in the morning we'll see what his choice may be."

The husband and wife then parted, but the conversation had given the lady cause to think and she made her preparations accordingly. First she went in search of her daughter

Meg, nicknamed by her thoughtless father "Muckle-mou'd Meg", although in truth she was, though plain, by no means unpleasing in appearance. At twenty-six, however, she had long assumed that she would never find a husband. Finding her daughter at her embroidery, the mother opened the conversation regarding the possibility of obtaining a husband.

"Here you are then, Meg, twenty-six years old and still unwed and I was just nineteen when I married your father," she began baldly. "Is it not time you did something about it?"

"That may be so," replied the unfortunate Meg. "But you are still a good-looking woman while I have never had your looks and that's the way of it. I'll not be finding a husband now. They don't grow on trees."

"There's one likely boy who may well grow on a tree if you do nothing about it. What about young Will Scott, for instance? Had you thought of trying him?" demanded her mother.

"But father has decreed that he shall hang tomorrow and father never changes his mind once he has given an order. I doubt if he'd change his mind even if Will was married to me," cried Meg. "Beside why should Will Scott of Harden look at me when he has all the countryside of Ettrick and for that matter far beyond to choose from?"

"That's a matter between your father and him," replied Lady Murray. "But if Will Scott decides to marry you it would not surprise me if your father agreed."

Meanwhile Sir Gideon had not taken long to put his wife's plan into action and, visiting the prisoners manacled in their dungeon, he put the matter to young Will Scott bluntly enough.

"Though you deserve hanging and, indeed, hanging's too good for you, I'll give you one chance of life yet, you young rogue," he said. "You can choose between hanging and marriage. Tomorrow morning you will either marry my daughter Meg, or you and your kinsman here will hang from the tree in my courtyard until the crows have pecked your skeleton clean and the bones have fallen to the ground to be eaten by the dogs. Make your choice for it's all one to me."

"Oh, Sir Gideon, God save us," cried Simon. "You'll not be wanting to hang me alone surely? Not when my master agrees to marry your daughter as I'm sure he will. You'll allow me at least the chance to dance at the wedding. And you, Master Will, surely you'll consent to marry the lass however old and ugly she may be? That's surely better than condemning us both to a needless death and my wife and children mourning?"

"Be silent, Simon," snapped the young laird. "As for you, Sir Gideon, you know well enough that if our positions were reversed and chance had placed your life in my hands I would hang you with as little ceremony as you propose to hang me. Your generous offer of your *bonny* daughter's hand I throw back in your face. Do your worst."

"Very well, you young rogue," replied Sir Gideon sternly. "On your own head be it. Tomorrow you will hang and let that be an end of it."

"Oh, Sir Gideon," interrupted Simon Scott earnestly. "Do not be in such a hurry. I am sure when he reconsiders the matter my master will realise that it is better to marry than hang in the morning, however plain his bride might be."

"Be quiet, you cowardly rogue," snapped Will Scott. "Do I hear a Scott trembling in the presence of a Murray?"

"If you will excuse me, sir, you hear nothing of the kind," answered Simon Scott earnestly. "I just do not see why two men should die when one of them can alleviate the situation by getting married. There's nothing so terrible about marriage, however plain the wife. Why Sir Gideon, come to that, should my wife die, which God forbid, and no-one else be available I'd always be willing to offer for one of your daughters myself."

"You impudent idiot, take that for your pains," roared Sir Gideon, striking the wretched Simon round the head.

"Shame on you, Sir Gideon, for striking a fettered and helpless prisoner," cried Will Scott. "Where is the pride of the Murrays now?"

95

Somewhat ashamed of himself, it seemed, Sir Gideon then left them somewhat abruptly, merely pausing to reiterate:

"Just remember. Tomorrow at noon, you will either marry my daughter or hang."

"Leave us alone," replied Will Scott impatiently. "I've given you my answer and I've no intention of changing my mind. Faced with that choice I'd rather hang any day."

When the door had shut behind the knight Simon Scott attempted once more to persuade his leader to change his mind.

"Oh, sir," he said earnestly. "Though she may not have the finest looks in the Borders I'm told the lass has good sense and an excellent temper and if you knew as well as I do what a difference that can make to a marriage you'd not be so hasty about turning the idea down out of hand."

"Oh, stop your snivelling, Simon," replied Will Scott shortly. "Remember you are a Scott and in the morning show them you can die like one, for my mind's made up and that's that."

A few hours later, when the evening shadows had fallen, the door of their prison was opened by the guard and a maiden entered.

"What do you want, lass?" demanded the young laird.

"I come to ask the Laird of Harden if he has any dying commands that I may fulfil," she replied. "Sir Gideon's lady, on whom I am attendant, has a mother's feeling for you, despite your refusal of her daughter, poor Meg. She shares a mother's feelings for you at such a time and wishes to know if you want any last message taken to your own mother and sisters. If so, I am here to take them for you at her command."

"Ah, do not speak to me of my mother," he begged her. "I cannot think of her without emotion and I wish to die as befits a Scott of Harden."

"Keep it up, lassie," whispered Simon Scott. "Keep telling him about his sorrowing mother and sisters and how sad they must be for him when all he has to do is marry Meg."

"What's that you are muttering, Simon?" demanded Will Scott sternly.

"I was just thinking you'd maybe like to write a letter to your mother, sir," Simon answered hastily.

"I have brought pen, ink and paper with me, sir, and you may write what you wish," the lass continued. "I will see that your mother receives it and mayhap have time to return with a reply from her."

"No," replied the young laird sadly. "I fear that by the time you have gone that far I will be hanging from the tree in the courtyard that Sir Gideon has chosen for the purpose. But, by heavens, my death will be avenged. Just tell my mother it was my last command that she should rally all the Scotts she can raise to attack the Laird of Elibank and burn his house to the ground so that he may rue the day he murdered a Laird of Harden."

"No, no, dear lass," interrupted Simon. "Just see if you cannot get Sir Gideon's good lady to persuade him to postpone matters for a few days and mayhap if my laird should meet Miss Margaret he might begin to see things differently."

"Now, now, Simon, enough of that," commanded the young laird. "By all means let the maiden approach her mistress to gain a reprieve for you, for Sir Gideon can gain nothing by your death, but as for me the matter is settled."

"Indeed, sir, you mistake my intention," replied Simon. "If we have to hang I'll hang with you willingly enough, but surely it is only rational at least to meet the young lady before you hang rather than marry her. After all you might even find you like her."

"And is it really true," asked the lass, "that you prefer the gallows to poor Meg without seeing her?"

"If I haven't seen her," the laird replied stubbornly, "at least I've seen her father and I'm told she favours him, poor lass."

"It may be, you know, that you've had an exaggerated picture painted of the poor girl," the maiden replied. "It's possible as your man here says that if you saw her you might even change your mind."

"Enough of that," replied the young laird brusquely. "I won't be forced into anything, especially not by Sir Gideon Murray. A Scott may be led but not driven. But you sound a good-hearted lass and if you'd just show us your face in the light I'd like a good look at you to see if I feel I can trust you with my last letter to my mother."

"I fear, sir, you'll find no more in my looks than you might expect of my poor Mistress Meg," she replied, throwing back her cloak from her face. "But I'd have you remember that a fine pearl may lie within an unsightly oyster shell."

'There's truth enough in that," admitted the young laird, looking earnestly at her in the light. "And I'll tell you now, my lass, that though you may not be beautiful, there's an honesty and kindliness shines from your face and even though you are a Murray I will trust you with a letter to my mother."

"And I will do my best to have your life spared at least until you receive her answer," replied the maiden unexpectedly. "For if I ask Lady Murray as a mother to grant that request I am sure she will do her best to persuade Sir Gideon to agree. At least I can but try. And speaking for myself, if I can think of a way for you to escape the gallows I will do my best to follow it through."

"Thank you, lassie, thank you," cried Simon. "Although my master refuses to marry your mistress, believe you me, if I were free I would have married her myself. But there's one small request I have for you. When you go to deliver the letter to his mother will you just go down to the riverbank to a little white house and there you'll find my wife and children, or should I say widow and orphans, and tell my wife I never knew how dear she was to me before and that if she marries again I'll come back and haunt her, and tell my children to look after her for me."

Meanwhile the laird had scribbled a few lines to his mother and, sealing the letter, he gave it to the girl and thanked her with a kiss before she left them.

The following morning Margaret Murray, Muckle-mou'd

Meg, as she had been so thoughtlessly nicknamed by him, went to see her father.

"I hear it is your pleasure, father, that I should marry young Will Scott of Harden. I feel, sir, it is due to your daughter, a Murray of Elibank, that she should be courted before she goes to the altar. The man has never met me and never even seen me and I will never disgrace you by giving my hand to a man who only took it to save his neck from the gallows. Before our marriage I would like some time to get to know the young man and I beg that you put off the hanging or the marriage for at least a week so that I can get to know him and decide for myself whether I wish to be his wife."

"Well said, Meg!" cried Sir Gideon. "I didn't realise you had the spirit in you to make such a request, but I am afraid it's useless for the lad has already resolutely refused you and he's due to hang at noon."

"Oh, don't take that for an answer, father," cried the girl. "Let me have at least four days to get to know him and if after that he doesn't ask to marry me without a dowry then I must look even worse than folk have a habit of saying."

"Very well, Meg," agreed the knight, rather reluctantly. "He shall have four days' grace, for your sake. Then if he refuses you again he shall hang in the courtyard and his half-witted follower with him."

With this assurance his daughter left him and hastened with all her speed to Harden where Will Scott's mother and sister who had learned of his capture in the raid on Elibank were already mourning his imminent death. Then came the announcement that a young lass was outside with a message from the captured laird and desired a word with her.

"Show her in," cried the young laird's mother. "Come in, lassie, and tell me what Will has to say?"

"He sent this short letter with me and I will be happy to take back any answer you may wish to make," replied the girl.

"And who are you, lassie? And why do you take the side of a Scott against the Murrays to whom you belong?" asked Will Scott's mother, the erstwhile "Flower of Yarrow".

"I am but a servant lass, yet I can have feelings like any other and there is little I would not do for as fine a young man as your son," replied the girl. "But that aside, my mistress, Lady Murray, feels for you as a mother and has commanded me to be of what help I can."

"Bless both you and her for those words," exclaimed the distracted mother, breaking the seal of the letter and reading her son's message.

"Dearest Mother – I am by ill chance a prisoner of Murray of Elibank and have been condemned to die. Do not mourn for me but rouse every Scott to revenge me as soon as may be possible. I have been offered my freedom if I would marry Murray's daughter, Muckle-mou'd Meg, but I have scorned such a suggestion."

"Ah, Will, my proud lad, you maybe thought you were right," cried his mother. "But for my sake I wish you had thought otherwise. Better by far to have married the lassie whatever she might be like."

Turning to the girl who had brought the message she put the question that came to her mind.

"What is this Margaret Murray like then ? Is she as ugly as they say?"

"She may not have the handsomest of features," replied the lass."But she is no worse, if no better, than me, for instance. Yet she has a very kindly nature and you might go a long way to find much better in that respect. On the whole you could find many a lass who'd make a worse wife than her."

"If it be as you say, then my poor rash Will should marry her and save his neck," declared his mother vehemently. "But the lad is just like his father and you might as well try to shift the Eildon hills as try to force him to do anything he did not want."

She finished the letter in which Will wrote praising the female bearer of his message and vowing that should he gain his freedom he would marry her regardless of her station and the fact that she might be a kinsman of the Murrays, even though he had refused Sir Gideon's daughter.

"Lassie," wept Lady Scott, "my son writes most warmly of your kindness to him and your wish to help him escape. I was wondering if perhaps I could go with you to Elibank and try to make the stubborn lad change his mind with a mother's pleas. Do you think that could be managed?"

"My lady," replied the maiden, "I can only do my best but I think it could be done and I can promise at least to see you safely back."

No sooner said than done and within a short space of time Lady Scott, disguised as an old peasant woman and carrying a basket over her arm, set out with the lass for Elibank. Meanwhile the sun's rays had just pierced the gloom of the dungeon where Will Scott and his kinsman Simon were chained.

"Oh, sir," Simon demanded. "Here's our last sight of the sun, for this is the day we are to be hanged. Will you not change your mind and marry the lass? Surely it's a small enough thing to ask?"

"For the last time, Simon," replied the young laird shortly, "will you stop your moaning. My mind is made up and there's an end of it."

At that moment the door was opened and a voice announced, "Sir Gideon Murray has spared your lives for another day so that Scott of Harden may have time to reflect on the offer that has been made to him."

The sun had again set and the dim lamp which illuminated their dank prison was flickering vainly against the dark shadows when the door opened and the maiden appeared again.

"Ah, lassie, lassie," cried Simon at the sight of her. "And tell me how are my wife and bairns? Are they well and how did they bear the news that they'll soon be losing me?"

"I did not have time to see them, sir," she replied. "But whether they will be losing you or not depends on your master."

"Speak not of that," cried Will Scott. "But tell me, how is my mother and has she promised to avenge my death?"

"She says she would rather gain a daughter than lose a

son," replied the lass. "And she begs that you will marry Sir Gideon's daughter."

"Has my mother gone as far as to suggest I marry the daughter of our old enemy?" cried Will. "I'll obey her in anything but that."

"But surely," pressed the lass, "you are wrong to reject poor Meg before you have even seen her. She may well be better looking than you had supposed. Don't forget that it would be very pleasant to hear the lark singing overhead and feel the wind on the moors in your face instead of resting in a cold grave. You do not have so long to live in this world at best and you have an eternity dead. Do you not feel that for your mother's sake, if nothing else, that you might change your mind?"

"Dear lass," he replied. "I appreciate the sincerity with which you speak, but I will never allow Sir Gideon Murray the satisfaction of being able to say that he frightened me into marrying his daughter. When my mother comes to think over my decision she will see it in that light too."

"Well, sir," replied the maiden, "if you will not listen to me perhaps you will listen to someone more persuasive than me?"

"What's this?" cried the young laird. "Who else have you with you? Have you been playing me false after all?"

"No, no! That's not possible," she answered. "But you shall see for yourself."

With that she opened the door and stepped outside and in a moment Lady Scott rushed in to embrace her son.

"Mother!" he cried in astonishment. "How did you get here? How is this?"

"Oh, my son," she wept. "Do not be stubborn any more. For your mother's sake, marry Sir Gideon's daughter and save your life. Do not break my heart."

"Mother," he cried again, "do you not realise that if they find you here Sir Gideon will demand a ransom for your return?"

"The clever lass that brought your letter contrived to get me here under promise of safe return," she replied. "And surely you see that the best thing you can do is marry Sir Gideon's daughter Meg. The lass assures me she is a good enough looking maid with an excellent disposition."

"Oh, how right you are, my lady," agreed Simon eagerly. "Just keep at him and make him see the error of his ways. There's no need for him and me to be hanged in the morn for the Murrays' amusement. After all if he marries her and finds he doesn't like her, he can always return her to her ancestral home. And surely you can make him see that marriage is a thousand times better than a hanging?"

"Simon, be quiet," commanded Will Scott. "Never shall a Murray be in a position to say he put fear into a Scott of Harden. My mind is as firmly fixed as his and our fate is fixed accordingly."

Despite his mother's entreaties he refused to change his mind and while they were still arguing with him the maiden returned.

"You must leave now, my lady," she said. "Sir Gideon will soon be down and if he were to find you here I would not be able to assist you further."

"Farewell, mother dear, farewell," cried young Will, embracing her.

"Oh, Will, I cannot bear to see you die this way," cried his mother. "Will you not yet change your mind for your mother's sake?"

"Ask it not," he replied firmly. "Farewell again for ever."

With that the maiden led her away and soon the sun rose once more, touching the dungeon with its rays. Finally the sound of spurred steps was heard outside their prison and the door creaked open yet again. There stood Sir Gideon frowning down on them.

"Now then, young Scott," he said. "What is your choice to be? A wife or the gallows?"

"Lead on to the gallows," replied the young laird scorn-fully. "Even with the rope round my neck I will spit on you and your offer."

"Guards, take Will Scott of Harden forth and hang him from the tree that is prepared for him," commanded Sir

Gideon. "But as for you," he added to Simon. "I have no quarrel with you and you can go free, but don't cross me again or you will certainly hang."

"No, sir," replied Simon stoutly. "I have no desire to hang, but if you hang my master, then you surely must hang me beside him, for where he goes, I go."

"Well, away with them both then," commanded the knight stamping his iron-shod foot on the ground so that sparks flew from the stones.

"Ah, well, if it must be, it must be," said Simon resignedly. "But I must say, master, you have acted very foolishly this day."

They were led from the dungeon and through the court-yard to the tall oak around which Sir Gideon's retainers were assembled to watch the execution. There the knight took his seat on the raised dais in front. It was at this moment when the hangman were preparing the captives for execution that his daughter Margaret approached him, heavily veiled, and went down on her knees before her father.

"A boon, father," she asked. "Your daughter asks a boon at this time."

"You choose an ill-timed moment to ask for it, Meg," cried the knight angrily. "But what may it be?"

She spoke earnestly in undertones to him for a few moments and his expression conveyed surprise and indignation, then softened into something more like resignation when at the end of her speech she knelt before him again and grasped his knee.

"Ah well, rise then, Meg," he said impatiently. "For your sake only and at your request, he shall have a final chance to live."

Drawing himself to his full height he then addressed his prisoner with the rope around his neck.

"William Scott," he said. "You have chosen death instead of the hand of my daughter. Will you now prefer to die rather than marry the lassie who took a letter to your mother and without my consent brought her to see you?"

"Had anyone other than you asked me that question," answered Will Scott, "I would have said No and offered the lass my hand, heart and fortune, but to you, Sir Gideon, I say only – do your worst!"

"Then Will, my dear Will," cried his mother, rushing forward from the throng. "Another does ask you to marry her and that your own mother."

"And," added Margaret throwing aside her heavy veil, "poor Margaret over whom you showed a preference for the gallows also asks you."

"What!" cried the young laird, grasping her hand. "Is the lass who helped me and my mother indeed the very same Margaret that I have been refusing to marry?"

"In truth I am," she smiled. "And do you now still prefer the gallows?"

"No indeed," he smiled in reply, and turning to Sir Gideon he added simply, "Sir, I am now willing to be married rather than hang."

"So be it," replied Sir Gideon, with an answering wry smile and the assembled Murrays cheered loudly, joined most heartily by Simon Scott.

Thus the day that had started with preparations for a hanging ended with a happy wedding. Will Scott, later himself knighted, and his father-in-law in after years rode and hunted together amicably enough, each to their surprise finding much in common with the other. Margaret, his wife, her unfortunate nickname soon forgotten, bore him sons and daughters, all as handsome as their father and as clever as their mother. Lady Margaret Scott soon proved as Sir William Scott proudly claimed one of the best wives in Scotland, while to Simon Scott she remained always one of the best-looking women in Ettrick Forest.

Harden Tower, as already noted, is four miles west of Hawick in Roxburghshire, now the home of Lord Polwarth. Elibank House, on the site of Sir Gideon Murray's Border Tower, stands five miles east of Innerleithen in Selkirkshire. They are separated by a good fifteen miles of rough country, as the crow flies, which is some indication of the distances the old Border reivers were prepared to travel on horseback by the light of the moon.

Innerleithen is a village on the river Tweed famed for its knitwear and makes a good base for exploring Tweedside and the surrounding country from Peebles to Kelso.

LORD MAXWELL'S OATH

This Tale covers the transitional period from the 1590s
through to the first decade of James VI's rule as King
of both Scotland and England. In the 1590s there was
a final outbreak of lawlessness in the Borders, but as
the century ended James VI, for the first time, began
to impose his will more firmly. With his accession to
the throne of England he began at last to impose a rule
of law in the Borders. Although generally vacillating
and ready to give way to determined pleas from his
advisors, in this instance he appears for once to have
stood firm and allowed justice to take its course.

IN THE 1590s, about ten years before James VI succeeded
to the throne of England, the long standing feud, which
had existed for generations between the Maxwells of
Nithsdale and the Johnstones of Annandale broke out yet
again with even more violence than previously. Several of
the lairds whose lands and property lay within the area
over which the two forces disputed most consistently and
who as a result had suffered damage, entered into a secret
pact with Lord Maxwell to both defend and attack in
unison as required. In the course of time, Sir James
Johnstone naturally learned about this and immediately
began to do his best to break up the league, which very
greatly increased his rival's power.

It seemed, however, as if the Maxwells were acquiring an

ascendancy which would make any real resistance hopeless. Sir James Johnstone in this extremity obtained the aid of the Scotts and other clans of the middle regions of the Borders. Lord Maxwell, on the other hand, as the King's Lieutenant, rallied round him the main barons of Nithsdale and set off to attack his opponents on their own ground.

Although Lady Maxwell had no particular fear for her husband's safety, she was naturally a little impatient when on the second day after his departure there was still no news, for it was unusual for her husband not to send a messenger ahead. As evening was falling, however she was told of a band of mosstroopers approaching from the east. She went up on to the battlements of Thrieve Castle, the ancient stronghold of the Maxwells situated on an island formed by the river Dee amidst wild moorland. There was still light enough to see the returning band clearly enough and they did not have the air of men returning victorious. Their beasts were tired and jaded, the men themselves appeared exhausted and downcast, with none of the shouts and laughter which usually distinguished Borderers returning from battle.

"Pray God nothing has happened," Lady Maxwell said to her daughters in alarm.

She had scarcely descended to the castle hall when her eldest son, a youth of twenty, approached her, alone.

"Your father?" asked Lady Maxwell. "I need not ask, of course. He is dead, is he not?"

Her son's silence showed that she was right, but in the manner of Border wives she did not show her emotions in public. She went stern-faced to her own chamber where she gave vent to her grief by herself. Meanwhile preparations for the evening meal were made and the exhausted soldiers ranged themselves along the table in the baronial hall while their young master took his father's accustomed place at the head. He would no doubt have preferred not to have to sit there and prove himself a good host in such circumstances, but it would have seemed as if he were lacking in hospitality had he not remained with his guests, several of whom were

108

barons only just inferior in rank to that he had so recently inherited.

When the troops in the hall had satisfied their hunger the events of the morning began to form the main topic of conversation, mainly in whispers and lowered tones. Lord Maxwell had encountered his opponents at Dryffe Sands, near to Lockerbie, and had been defeated partly through the cowardice of his own supporters, whose alliance with him had been the initial cause of the renewed outbreak of hostility. He had been struck from his horse as he fled and although he begged for quarter his assailant had struck off his hand and slaughtered the unfortunate baron without mercy. Many of his followers had been killed too and most were wounded, particularly by slashes about the face, known thereafter as Lockerbie Licks. The young Lord Maxwell, having left behind sufficient men to repel any attempt to follow them, had then withdrawn to Thrieve Castle to decide on what measures to take next.

After the discussions of the evening had ended and the exhausted soldiers had retired to bed, Lady Maxwell summoned her son to her chamber and demanded to know what he intended to do.

"Orchardstone talks of a bond," replied young Maxwell, referring to his older cousin Sir James Maxwell of Orchardstone Tower.

"A bond of alliance! And did you listen to him?" demanded the dowager, looking at him keenly. "Did you let him repeat the word? Talk not to me of peace! Talk not to me of bonds! Talk of revenge! Remember that the blood of him who has been treacherously slain runs in your veins. You got no craven heart from him and you have none from me. Why then do you stand thus dumb and wavering?"

"Madam, you have forestalled me," the young man replied. "I will have revenge. The King –"

"What! Would you play the spaniel to James!" she interrupted. "A craven sovereign worthy of a craven suitor. My boy, will you break my heart outright? This comes of the monkish upbringing of that old man whom your father brought to this house, not to make a coward of his son, but to shelter a frightened priest from persecution."

"Madam! Let me speak, if you please," replied the young man proudly. "I am neither coward nor craven as you seem to think. Nor am I a child that needs to be spurred with harsh speeches. My father's blood boils as fiercely in my veins as the blood of Douglas in yours. Our deliberations are not at an end and by daybreak tomorrow they will be resumed."

"Ah, but, my son, you do not say you will seek revenge," cried Lady Maxwell. "You speak of these minor barons with whom you demean yourself by consulting. Your father told them what his will would be and did not ask them what they wished. It was their duty to obey him as it is their duty to obey you, if you will but make your orders plain."

"Why do you have to speak so harshly?" demanded her son. "Have I not borne myself like my equals and my name? But you shall not lack for the revenge you demand. This house and all that is in it are yours until revenge is also yours. My life shall have but one object and one end until that is achieved."

"Wait, my son, wait," Lady Maxwell interrupted in a calmer tone. "You have said enough, indeed more than enough to satisfy my doubts. I would not remain sole lady of this castle."

"The oath is recorded in heaven. The words have been said and may not be recalled," replied the young lord implacably.

After receiving his mother's blessing, Lord Maxwell retired to his bed chamber and although he foresaw a day of difficult and tough discussion ahead, the day's events had tired him to the extent that he had no difficulty in sleeping. He continued sleeping peacefully through till the next morning when the priest to whom his mother had referred entered and woke him.

The elderly priest was a kinsman of the young lord who had entered the Roman Catholic church and been given sanctuary by the Maxwells. He had acted as tutor to the young man and there was an affection between them. Now he was deeply concerned, because he knew the course the young man was likely to take and he was determined to try to save him from it.

"I know that the rules of the old Border warfare require you to avenge the death of your father," he said. "But you and I have discussed such a situation many times and you have agreed with me that it is wrong. I trust that you will now instead enter into an alliance with the Johnstones. Or do you intend to let these barons who are here with you persuade you to take what you know is the wrong course?"

"I am bound by an oath which I cannot break," replied the young man sadly. "I have made a solemn vow to seek revenge and it must stand regardless."

"Ah, but my dear boy," countered the old priest. "An oath which has an evil objective may be honourably broken. The honour and strength of mind is indeed in breaking it, not in abiding by it."

"Ah," replied the young Lord Maxwell. "but the oath is no longer in my keeping and anyway I would not break it if I could. It may be that an evil oath should be broken, but I am not highly versed in such obscure matters."

"And more's the pity," replied the priest. "I had hoped you would prove an honour to your name and to your country and that you might lead the way forward in healing the wounds of this embattled land."

"Forgive me, my old friend and mentor," replied young Maxwell sadly. "My fate is fixed irretrievably and my actions are reserved for a narrower sphere. My father's blood cries out for vengeance and that I have sworn he shall have, come what may."

Taking a fond farewell of his old friend he went into the council chamber where his barons were assembled. They were considerably divided as to whether or not they should enter into alliance with the Johnstones. So strongly, however, did Lord Maxwell call on them for support against the Johnstones that they immediately began preparations for further warfare.

111

From then on for several weary years the area was plunged into continual warfare between the opposing factions. Many atrocities were carried out by either side despite warnings, threats and entreaties from the King, all of which were ignored. As his elderly relative had feared, young Lord Maxwell became accustomed to scenes of bloodshed and suffering and pursued his vindictive campaign of hatred against his older and more experienced foe with a bitterness which excelled the experience of any living Borderers. Some five or six years after the battle of Dryffe Sands Sir James Johnstone was appointed Warden of the Middle Marches and Lord Maxwell took advantage of his absence to ravage his territory with even more ferocious ardour than before. Hearing of this, James VI, by now on the throne of England, sent reinforcements to his rival with orders to banish Lord Maxwell from the Borders.

Angry and disappointed, Lord Maxwell was offered shelter by his cousin, the Marquis of Hamilton, at Craignethan Castle in Clydesdale. Despite the best efforts of his cousin and his sister Lady Margaret, or their mother, nothing they could do seemed to drive away the gloom in which their still young and handsome relative was plunged. He spent most of his day sitting amongst beautiful scenery contemplating plans for revenge on his hated rival. While he was thus sitting wrapped in gloomy thought he heard a charming female voice singing the familiar Border song *Johnny Armstrong's Last Goodnight*. Supposedly sung by Johnny Armstrong the famous Border reiver the night before he was hung by King James V at Gilnockie, the verses suited his mood admirably;

> *This night is my departing night.*
> *For here nae longer must I stay;*
> *There's neither friend nor foe of mine,*
> *But wishes me away.*
>
> *What I have done through lack of wit,*
> *I never, never can recall;*
> *I hope you're a' my friends as yet –*
> *Good night and joy be with you all.*

112

The sweet voice of the singer held him entranced until the song was over, when he sprang to his feet and went in search of the singer but could find no one. For the moment, however, his spirits had been lifted. Only as he returned to the castle, aware that he must attend a festive dinner that evening, did the black mood seize him again for he was still in no mood for company other than his own.

Later that evening at the dinner table a young French Count who was present began an argument with a Scotsman as to which of the two countries produced the better music. After some argument they were each persuaded to give a sample of their country's songs and Lord Maxwell was called on to adjudicate as to which was best. Since there was considerable laughter and jeers when they had each finished singing, no one present was expecting any serious judgment on that issue, but Lord Maxwell took the opportunity of addressing his host.

"Although I don't wish to judge which is the better singer of the two," he said, "I think I could convince our French friend that Scottish melodies when well sung are at least the equal of those of his own country, about which he is so passionate, but you must help me."

"Just tell me how," replied the Marquis, delighted to see his cousin beginning to show an interest in matters other than his vengeful quest.

"While I was in your woods today," Maxwell replied. "I heard a lass singing *Johnnie Armstrong's Last Goodnight* and whoever it was disappeared before I could find who had made that simple song sound so bewitching. If our friend could hear that songstress the dispute would be at an end. But who it was I do not know, though it may be that you do."

"I can tell you who it was," replied the Scot who had taken the side of Scottish music and turned towards his host's sister, Lady Margaret. "Lady Margaret will sing it for you and our French friend will have to eat his words about Scottish music."

It was indeed Lady Margaret who had been singing and when he heard her voice again singing that song of his

113

native Borders Lord Maxwell experienced a strong emotion compounded of homesickness and longing for a more ordered life. The French Count was at once converted to the cause of Scottish music and started paying such outrageous compliments to his wife's sister that Lord Maxwell was roused to emulate and even outdo him. As the following days lengthened into weeks, much of which was spent in her company, he fell unconsciously in love with her.

Some months passed and the Marquis himself was about to marry. Noticing the ripening relationship between his sister and his cousin, he joked about Lord Maxwell's continuing bachelor state, maintaining that he himself had never been so happy since he had decided on marriage.

"And why may I not remain a bachelor and be just as happy as you?" demanded Maxwell.

"Might not my sister make you change your mind on that state of affairs?" demanded the Marquis.

Lord Maxwell looked stricken as these words sank into his mind. He realised that for several months he had totally forsaken his oath and had been idling away his time, albeit in the most delightful way. His conscience suddenly pierced him like a spear. His solemn oath to his mother which had guided all his actions over the past years recurred in his mind like a clap of thunder. His heart felt crushed within him and he stood pale and unspeaking for some time until his cousin grasped his hand in alarm at the sudden change in his young relation.

"What is it?" he demanded. "What's the matter? Are you all right?"

"Yes . . . yes!" replied Lord Maxwell in distracted tones. "But I had forgotten. I must go! I have been here too long already. I must leave at once!"

"But why?" asked the Marquis. "Surely nothing I have said has offended you that you must leave so suddenly?"

"No, no," answered the other distractedly. "I am not offended at anything. It is just that I have only this instant recalled my oath. It is just that I have only this moment regained my senses. I must not remain here a minute longer. My father's death is unavenged. I have forgotten my task and broken my oath. I must fulfil the first and redeem the other."

"What task? What oath?" demanded the bewildered Marquis.

"I have told you the task," replied Lord Maxwell impatiently. "To revenge my father's death! I have sworn that until the life's blood of his murderer is staining the earth I will not rest by day or night. I will not enjoy land or power or life itself until that has been accomplished."

He paused uncertainly for a moment.

"If your sister would deign to consider me," he added. "She may regard me as her humble suitor whenever Johnstone lies dead and my duty has been fulfilled."

All the arguments the Marquis put forward to restrain him proved in vain. Despite the order of banishment, he left Craignethan Castle that day and returned to his own home at Thrieve Castle. Within a matter of days he was organising preparations for a raid on the Johnstone land and news of his return had spread throughout the area. It did not take long for Sir James Johnstone to learn of his intentions and muster his men, along with royal reinforcements, in preparation for any attack.

The Maxwell attack on the Johnstone forces took place not far from the scene of the previous bloody conflict at Dryffe Sands. The Johnstones had the advantage of rising ground and a good defensive position. They were not taken unawares as Lord Maxwell had hoped, indeed it was soon plain that he had led his own men into a trap prepared by a wilier and more experienced enemy.

Despite his own courageous leadership and the efforts of his men, who fought long and hard against the superior forces of the Johnstones, they were eventually forced to retreat with scarcely a man unwounded. Although urged to go with them, Lord Maxwell himself refused to turn his back on his old enemy. In a last desperate charge he rushed into their midst striking with his sword at all and sundry.

"Take him alive!" came the cry.

Finally, exhausted, wounded and overwhelmed by sheer weight of numbers he was felled from his horse and made prisoner. Then, after remaining some days in Annandale, he was conveyed to Edinburgh under armed escort and imprisoned in the castle. There his desire for revenge was increased by his own sense of personal injury at the hands of his enemy. He spent his time brooding on his real and imagined grievances and swearing once more a fearful vengeance on his enemy.

Meanwhile Lady Margaret Hamilton was not unhappy at the news that her young cousin was to be found in Edinburgh and she turned over in her mind various plans for his release. To some extent this was prompted by the approach of an old and loyal clansman of Lord Maxwell's named Charlie of Kirkhouse. As well as being a loyal follower of his chief, Charlie was shrewd and able, but he knew that to plan his master's escape he would need all the help he could get. With this in mind he had approached Lady Margaret, who had advised him to try to gain employment in the King's forces as a disaffected follower of Maxwell.

It was not a difficult task to enlist in the King's men employed at the castle and once there he sought to gain the confidence of his superiors by roundly cursing his master as a tyrant and hard taskmaster. Unfortunately he found himself under a Johnstone clansman, Will of Gummerlie, who took pleasure in bullying one whom he disliked as a hereditary enemy. Charlie, however, did his best to ingratiate himself with other superior officers in the hope this might lead to an opportunity to help his master to escape.

Charlie was on guard duty one day when one of his fellow gaolers appeared with a young man, whose hat was pulled well down over his face.

"Who is this then, Charlie?" asked the soldier.

"I can't say I know," replied Charlie, glancing at the youth.

"Can you not guess who he is?" demanded the soldier.

"I am Lord Maxwell's brother," said the young man, stepping closer to Charlie. "Do you not recognise me?"

"His brother?" demanded Charlie, well aware that the young man in question was a much burlier figure.

"Yes, his brother, Charlie," replied the youth, stepping forward and raising his hat slightly and revealing his face. "Do you not recognise me?"

"Oh, yes, indeed," he replied. "I recognise you now, all right."

"Then he is Lord Maxwell's brother?" demanded the guard.

"Who else would he be?" replied Charlie, turning away and resuming his sentry duties.

The young man was duly admitted into Lord Maxwell's prison, which consisted of a small room with bars across the narrow window high up in the castle walls.

"Your brother to see you, my Lord," announced the gaoler. "I'll return in half an hour."

Lord Maxwell was seated at a table with a book in his hand and now he rose and came forward.

"My brother Charles!" he exclaimed. "I thought you were in London! But what's this, why you're not half the man Charles is. Who is this?"

Then in the semi-darkness of the cell he recognised his visitor.

"Have you forgotten that song *Johnnie Armstrong's Last Goodnight?*" asked a well-remembered voice.

"No, nor your singing of it either, Lady Margaret," he replied. "But what good spirit has brought you here?"

"I have brought you the means of escape," she replied. "You can disguise yourself in my cloak and hat; the gaoler will not know the difference in this half-darkness and the sentry at the end of the court is Charlie of Kirkhouse, who will act as your guide and guard to the gate. The cloak and hat will deceive any others, who may have noticed me coming into the castle."

"No, no, it will not do," replied Lord Maxwell. "Even if I were to escape detection, I would not have you subjected to the rudeness of my gaolers when they discovered I was gone."

117

"I wish that I could persuade you to try, my dear," she replied affectionately. "Just as I wish that I could prevail on you to give up your schemes for vengeance to spend your energies instead on the good of your country and hear sounds of merriment and joy in your houses rather than sadness and mourning because of the loss of friends and loved ones in needless warfare."

"I wish that I could prevail on myself," replied Lord Maxwell ruefully. "And be content to pass my days in peace and happiness with none save one to care for. But I forget myself. This cannot be, I fear!"

"And why not, pray?" demanded Lady Margaret. "If you will but sign a bond renouncing all intent of renewing your hereditary warfare you would be freed at once and my brother would pledge his life and land for your word."

"Oh, do not tempt me any more!" replied the young man. "My will was weak and wavering, but I have not yet renounced my vow. You have spoken of hereditary foes and shall I be the first of my line to cast aside the fight? Happiness is but a dream, I know now. In a little while, dear lady, you will leave me and with you the dream will end."

In spite of everything Lady Margaret could say, the wilful young baron remained inflexible. However he agreed to try to escape if she would pass word to Charlie of Kirkhouse to see what help he could provide. As she left the castle Lady Margaret duly passed this message to Charlie as he paced the battlements on sentry duty.

After Lady Margaret's appearance Lord Maxwell turned his mind more forcibly to the possibility of escape. He started attempting to tunnel his way through the walls, but progress was so slow that he felt it would require more than a lifetime before he succeeded. As the days passed, however, he fell into a routine. Each day before the gaoler came with his evening meal he carefully tidied away the signs of his work on the wall. One evening, however, the gaoler did not merely place his meal on the table but, locking the door behind him, half-turned to the prisoner.

"Would you like to escape tonight, my Lord?" he asked.

"Charlie of Kirkhouse, as I breathe!" exclaimed Lord Maxwell. "How did you get here?"

"I'll tell you the tale of it later, my Lord,"replied Charlie, taking off his uniform overcoat. "Just you put on this uniform and hat and walk out of here as the gaoler. I'll remain in your place."

"But you must not run into danger on my account," protested his chief.

"Danger! What danger?" replied Charlie. "They'll not bother with the likes of me. You just do what I say."

Lord Maxwell was soon persuaded and, donning Charlie's outer coat and hat, he left Charlie in his place and marched boldly out through the main gate. There was a moment or two of suspense when the sentry wished to tell him a joke and was somewhat hurt when his friend Charlie merely greeted it with a grunt. The alarm was not raised, however, and he walked out to freedom. Once outside the castle he soon provided himself with a horse and by next morning was home again at Thrieve Castle.

At around the same time the gaoler unsuspectingly entered Lord Maxwell's chamber and was seized by the body and bundled into a closet before he knew where he was. Charlie then boldly walked down towards the main entrance and might well have got clean away had not the cries of the gaoler alerted the guard. Charlie was then seized. His old enemy Will of Gummerlie ordered him flogged with four dozen of the best before he was cast out of the castle.

"I'll see that repaid with interest, Will, my bonnie lad," he vowed to himself as he left and started the long journey on foot to Thrieve to join his lord.

Meanwhile Lord Maxwell had found that times had changed now that James VI was firmly ensconced on the throne of England. The barons who would formerly have answered his call to arms or suffered at the hands of his retainers refused to join what seemed a hopeless cause. Weary of endless warfare with their neighbours, most of them not only refused but made their objections to the suggestion plain.

After some weeks spent in ineffectual attempts to rally some followers to his cause, Lord Maxwell finally approached Sir Robert Maxwell of Orchardstone, who was related to Sir James Johnstone by marriage. Through him he proposed a meeting with Sir James Johnstone to see whether he might be prevailed on to intercede for him with the King. Flattered at this first sign of any conciliatory gesture, the elderly Sir James agreed to a meeting and the two chiefs attended at the appointed spot accompanied by a small group of followers.

Leaving most of their men at some distance, Sir Robert Maxwell of Orchardstone accompanied Sir James Johnstone and Will of Gummerlie to meet Lord Maxwell accompanied by Charlie of Kirkhouse.

"I hope you're no worse for your stay in the castle, Charlie?" Will greeted the latter sneeringly

"No thanks to you," replied Charlie, his temper rising. "I'll have it out of your hide one of these days, my lad. Just you watch out."

"Ha, ha, ha," jeered the other. "Are you still sore then?"

"Don't anger me!" snapped Charlie, drawing his pistol. "I warned you to watch out. So now take that!"

Raising his pistol he shot the unsuspecting Will of Gummerlie through the heart and he rolled from his saddle in his death throes.

Sir James Johnstone, hearing the shot, turned round to see what had happened and Lord Maxwell promptly put two bullets into his back. As the unfortunate man fell from his horse both Lord Maxwell and Charlie of Kirkhouse turned and galloped off with their followers to Thrieve. Here a large company was gathered to celebrate, as they thought, the reconciliation between the two clan chiefs and also the marriage of Lord Maxwell to Lady Margaret Hamilton. Lord Maxwell immediately approached his cousin the Marquis of Hamilton and told him of what had happened. He then asked him to tell his bride-to-be, to learn whether she wished to marry a man who had just shed blood in such a way.

"But he has slain his enemy in honourable battle," replied Lady Margaret. "Even if he has to be banished for a season the King has pardoned greater offences than that."

When this was reported to Lord Maxwell he could not help sneering at himself.

"Honourable battle, indeed!" he cried. "Would that it had been so. But I will not tell her the truth at this stage."

The wedding duly took place and the following morning, leaving his bride in tears behind him, Lord Maxwell and Charlie of Kirkhouse took to the road in disguise and were soon on a ship for France. Notwithstanding all the efforts of the Marquis of Hamilton, King James refused him a pardon.

For three or four years in the prime of his life, with all that he held dear remaining behind in Scotland, Lord Maxwell remained in exile. Nor could he forget that his revenge had been accomplished by meanly pistolling his enemy unawares. After some four years he learned that Lady Margaret was pining, then that she was ill and finally that her life was slipping away. He resolved regardless of his fate to return to Scotland, but before he returned his wife had died, heartbroken at the absence of her husband and the scandalous tale of his revenge on his enemy.

Hearing of his return, Sir James Johnstone's family set about hunting their enemy and eventually tracked him down in the wilds of Caithness. From there he was brought to Edinburgh once more. Here he was indicted for murder and put on trial. He was found guilty, for he made no defence, and condemned to be beheaded, with his estates forfeited to the crown.

On the night before his execution Sir Robert Maxwell of Orchardstone, now a very old man, visited his kinsman and chief in the company of the Marquis of Hamilton.

"Oh that it has come to this at last," groaned the old man. "If only you had listened to me eighteen years ago when I begged you to make a bond with Sir James Johnstone after your father's death. Do please make your peace with God. Some priest may be able to soothe your mind at least."

"Do not mock me, my uncle," replied Lord Maxwell in a bitter tone of voice. "Do not torture me with talk of peace of mind. I cannot have happiness in earth or heaven. I am content with what I have had. One gleam of sunshine has crossed my path for a few days. One human heart has been mine. My cup of bliss is full. One drop filled it. Leave me, I beg you. I would bless you, but it may turn out a curse."

His friends left him sorrowfully and the next day he was beheaded. His estates were forfeited. After a few years however the attainder was lifted and the honours and estates were conferred on his brother Charles.

Built by the Douglases in the fourteenth century, the ruins of Threave Castle (the modern spelling) stand impressively on an islet in the river Dee just over a mile west of Castle Douglas. It was only owned by the Maxwells for a short period in the sixteenth century.

The Maxwells of Orchardton, (also the modern spelling) died out in the late eighteenth century. Orchardton Tower, however, is an interesting and quite well preserved ruin, sited in a bowl in the hills and close to the sea. It is unusual in that it is a circular Peel tower, the only one of its kind in Scotland. It was built about the middle of the fifteenth century by John Cairns.

Castle Douglas and Dumfries both make good centres for touring this area. With its many Burns associations Dumfries is a popular tourist centre and an attractive town in its own right.

ARCHIE ARMSTRONG AND
FINGERLESS DICK

Tarras Moor, where this tale starts, was for a long time a stronghold of the Armstrongs. When besieged there on one occasion by Sir John Carey, English Warden of the East March, a party of Armstrongs stole out by night over the bog and returned with some of his cattle. They then presented him with one of his own beasts "in case he should run short of provisions while in Scotland".

It was on Tarras Moor that the famous reiver "Little Jock" Elliot was being closely chased by the Earl of Bothwell, Scots Warden of the Middle March, when the latter found himself bogged. Although himself wounded, Jock Elliot turned back and ran the Warden through with his dagger. It was this which persuaded Mary to make her dramatic and ill-advised journey to visit him as he lay badly wounded at Hermitage Castle. It also gave rise to the characteristically defiant border ballad with the memorable lines:

> *I vanquished the Queen's Lieutenant,*
> *And gar'd his fierce troopers flee,*
> *My name is Little Jock Elliot,*
> *And wha' daur meddle wi' me?*

With the accession of James VI to the throne of England as James VI of Scotland and I of England, the end of border reiving came at last. Admittedly it was a hard task controlling the unruly elements, as this Tale demonstrates. Many were in fact transported or fled to Northern Ireland, although many were also hung. A considerable number on both sides of the Border, however, found a new and profitable livelihood to be made from smuggling, since there were no excise duties in Scotland. Silks and spirits from the continent were easily transported over the border and a thriving industry with little of the old dangers soon developed.

IN THE last days of Elizabeth's reign the Borderers, in many cases, still carried on as of old, raiding their neighbours either side of the border and living by the only law they knew:

> *The good old law, the simple plan.*
> *That they should take who have the power,*
> *And they should keep who can.*

Amongst the foremost of the reivers then was Sandy Armstrong who lived at Cleughfoot in the centre of Tarras Moor, in a square tower of immense strength which could only be approached by winding and unknown paths through the bottomless bog. His wife Elspeth had borne him seven sons, but in various forays five of them had been slain and a sixth had been devoured by a bloodhound. His youngest, Archie, was all he had left to whom he could bequeath his stronghold, a fleet horse and his sword, for he had nothing else to leave. He had no land and had been brought up by his father to raid his neighbours' flocks or cattle when he felt the need. For thirty years he had lived in this way and knew no other.

In April 1603 Sandy Armstrong and some like-minded friends had been out on a raid on Penrith. In that desperate struggle some of them had been slain, others had been seized and executed at Carlisle, but Sandy had returned successfully, driving before him a score of oxen and half a dozen fine horses back to Cleughfoot. He had not heard the news of Elizabeth's death and the accession of James VI. Had he done so he would probably not have appreciated that this could mean the end of the border reiving by which he had lived. Being blissfully unaware of outside events, however, he was unconcerned as he took his favourite seat on the flat roof of Cleughfoot Tower and, between sups of aqua vitae from a stoup beside him, imparted Border wisdom to his young son Archie, a lad of twelve years.

Meanwhile James VI made his triumphal way south to take over the throne of England as well as Scotland. In Berwick he was greeted at Lamberton outside the town by the Marshal Sir John Carey at the head of the garrison, mounted and on foot. They then turned and marched back to the town where they lined the streets to the Marygate where he was presented with the keys of the town by William Selby. Selby knelt on one knee as he presented the keys of the town to his king. James VI promptly returned the keys and said;

"Rise, Sir William Selby, the first knight we have made as King of England and Scotland likewise, which you may take as no small honour."

He then met the Mayor and burgess of the town who presented him with a purse of gold, which was graciously received. This was followed by numerous ceremonies and a solemn church service. That evening there was a banquet and scenes of great rejoicing. The following day a messenger arrived with the news that the Armstrongs and others had committed serious depredations in the Borders and even carried their raid as far as Penrith.

"Borders, man!" said the King. "Our kingdom has no *borders* but the sea. It is our royal pleasure that the word *borders* shall cease to be used. What was once the *extremities or borders* of the two kingdoms are but the *middle of our kingdom*. In future it is our will and decree that they shall no longer be called the borders but the *middle counties*. And now, Sir William Selby, as we have but yesterday conferred on you the high honour of knighthood, take you two hundred and fifty horsemen and go through our middle counties commanding every true man in our name capable of bearing arms to join you in crushing and punishing such thieves and reivers. Hang each Armstrong and Maxwell or Johnstone that resists our royal will – reduce their strongholds to rubble and turn the iron bars of their towers into ploughshares. Off with you, sir, at once, and do your work surely and quickly."

The next day Sir William set forth and within a short time found himself at the head of a thousand horsemen. They burned and destroyed the border strongholds as they went and the more desperate men who fell into their hands were sent in irons to Carlisle to be tried and hung. Behind them they left a countryside transformed.

In early May when Tarras Forest was coming into leaf and the smell of Spring was in the air, Archie Armstrong was again seated on the flat roof of Cleughfoot Tower with his son Archie beside him.

"Archie, my son," said the reiver. "The world is turning upside down and honest men have no chance left in it. Nowadays we hear of nothing but Law! Law! Law! A man cannot take a beast or two in an honest way or make a bonfire out of an enemy's haystack or they end up in Carlisle with a hempen tie round their throat. But mind, laddie, you have the blood of the Armstrongs in your veins and their hands never earned bread by any instrument but the sword. It will not be the son of Sandy of Cleughfoot who disgraced his kith and kin by trudging behind a plough or some such beggarly way of earning a living. Swear to me, Archie, that you will live by the sword like your fathers before you and fear neither James Stuart, his two kingdoms or his horsemen. They'll be stout hearts that cross Tarras Moss and there will be few sheep in Liddesdale before the pot at Cleughfoot needs filling."

"I will live like my father before me – king of Tarras side," replied young Archie solemnly.

"That you will, Archie," said the reiver. "Though the Scotts and the Elliots may make their allegiance to the King

126

and get land for their bent knees, what cares Sandy Armstrong for their lands? His two-handed blade and his Jedhart axe shall be a better title to an Armstrong than an acre of parchment."

He crossed his arms and sat thoughtfully for a few moments before continuing.

"Archie, my son," he went on, "you're a brave lad, but this is no longer a brave man's country. Courage is persecuted, that's what it is. You had six brothers and they were all courageous lads. With them behind me I could have ridden north or south and made the name of Archie Armstrong feared. But they are all gone and there's none but you left to defend your mother when I am gone too. And now they would hunt me like the deer, for they are butchering good men for that small raid on Penrith as though the life of an Armstrong was of less value than an English loon. If you live to be a man, Archie, and when your mother is beneath the sod, leave this pitiful king-ridden land and take my sword to foreign lands where you may still live as decent men should."

At that moment the sleuth-hound which lay at their feet sprang alert and sniffed the air, then gave a long drawn out growl.

"What is it, Wolf? What is it, boy?" cried Sandy, springing to his feet.

"Troopers! Troopers, father!" cried Archie, whose keen sight had spotted them afar off. "And coming from all sides of the forest!"

"Get ready the pistols, Archie," cried the reiver. "It's two long spearheads to the bottom of Tarras moss and they'll be light men and lighter horses that do not find a grave in it. Just get ready the pistols and hot lead will welcome the first man that mentions King James's name before the walls of Cleughfoot."

The boy ran and brought his father's pistols and his mother accompanied him to the turret. She looked earnestly out on the approaching mass of horsemen for some minutes then took her husband's hand.

"Sandy," she said. "I have long expected this. But others that are wives now will go to bed tonight as widows as well as Elspeth Armstrong!"

"Fear nothing, Elspeth, my love," replied the reiver undaunted. "There will be blood in the way if they attack the lion in his den. But there's a long and tangled path between them and Cleughfoot over the Moss. We have seen enemies nearer who were glad to turn back again."

"They will reach us, father," cried Archie. "Do you not see they have masked traitors with them leading the way?"

In such cases, where a local man was betraying his neighbours, it was customary for them to wear masks, or hoods, while doing so to preserve their names and identity from the possibility of revenge. In the lead there were several masked men clearly to be seen.

"Ha! If they have masked men with them, your father is betrayed!" exclaimed the reiver. "So there's nothing for it but revenge and death for Sandy Armstrong!"

With those words he walked round the tower and carefully examined his pistols, the edge of his sword, his Jedhart axe and his spear. His wife Elspeth placed a steel cap on his head and from under it his dark hair, streaked with grey here and there, fell upon his forehead. He stood with his heavy spear in one hand and a pistol in the other on the topmost point of his tower. The setting sun sent his shadow across the moss to the very feet of the horses of the advancing troopers. Still the horsemen slowly approached from every side. Although the morass was impenetrable to strangers the masked traitors led them on by winding routes until they arrived within pistol shot of Cleughfoot.

"What want you, friends?" shouted the reiver. "Do you think that a poor man like Sandy Armstrong can provide food and shelter for five hundred horse?"

"We come," replied the officer leading the force, "by the authority of our gracious King James, King of both England and Scotland, in the name of his commissioner Sir William Selby to punish and bring to justice all the Border thieves

128

and outlaws, of whom, Sandy Armstrong of Cleughfoot, we are assured you are amongst the chief."

"You lie! You lie!" replied the reiver boldly. "I have lived these fifty years by my own hand and the man was never born who dared say that Sandy Armstrong ever laid a hand on a widow's cow or a poor man's mare. I have always been protector to the poor and helpless and defender of the weak-hearted in return for a small but honest payment."

"Do you surrender in peace, you boasting rebel?" demanded the herald. "Or must we burn your den about your ears?"

"It's death for me either way!" replied Sandy Armstrong. "You would show me and mine the same mercy that was shown to my kinsman John of Gilnockie and I shall surrender only as an Armstrong surrenders – when the breath is out of my body."

Fire flashed from a narrow arrow slit in the turret and the report of a pistol followed. The herald's horse bounded beneath him and fell dead.

"That was not done like an Armstrong, Archie," said the reiver reprovingly. "You shot the horse and might well have shot the rider. The man was only doing his duty and it was unfair and cowardly to fire on him until the battle had begun."

"I shan't forget again, father," replied Archie. "But I thought with such odds against us that every advantage taken was fair enough."

While this was going on Elspeth was laying loaded pistols and balls upon the roof of the turret. She also brought up a carbine which she put into her husband's hands.

"Take that, Sandy, to aim at their leaders," she said. "And leave the pistols to Archie and me."

The horsemen now surrounded the walls of Cleughfoot. Sandy, his wife and son knelt in the turret keeping up a hurried, but deadly fire on the besiegers. It was clear the enemy intended to blow up the outer wall. The reiver saw the train laid and the match applied. Already he had fired his last bullet.

"Let us fire the straw among the cattle in the courtyard," cried young Archie.

"A good thought, my son," cried the reiver. "Go to it!"

The lad rushed down the stairs to the house and returned with a flaming pine torch. He dropped it amongst the cattle and followed it with a handful of gunpowder and in a moment half the courtyard burst into flame. At the same instant a part of the outer wall trembled, exploded and fell inwards. The cattle and horses were running to and fro wildly in the courtyard through the fire. The invaders burst through the gap and met the panic-stricken beasts. Elspeth tore a pearl from her ear, loaded her pistol and fired it at the head of the first man to approach the tower.

It was clear they next intended to blow up the house as they had done the wall. Sandy now had no weapon left that he could use effectively except his spear.

"They shall taste the prick of the hedgehog before I die," he cried savagely and thrust down furiously at the advancing invaders.

Several fell backwards at his threshold, but the shaft was at last grabbed by one of their number and jerked from his grasp. By this time the sun had set and darkness was gathering over the bog outside. The fire still burned and the cattle rushed wildly to and fro amongst the armed men outside, but there was a temporary pause as the raiders regrouped themselves.

"Elspeth," cried the reiver. "It's not your life they seek and they'll not want to kill the child. Give me my Jedhart axe in my hand and farewell to you, my Elspeth – farewell – a last farewell for eternity! Archie, my gallant laddie, never disgrace your father and if I am murdered, mind you revenge me. Now we must unbar the door and I'll see if I cannot cut my way through them."

As the reiver spoke he embraced his wife and son and then seized his doubled-headed axe in his hands.

"Now, Archie," he whispered. "Slip down and unbar the door as softly as you can and stand back to let me rush out when you swing it wide."

Archie silently drew back the iron bars which held it bolted in place. In a moment the door swung back and Archie Armstrong was in the courtyard amongst his enemies, roaring like a raging lion and laying about them so wildly and relentlessly that a man fell at every stroke and those nearest shrank back from his whirlwind onslaught.

There was no man amongst them who had not heard of the terrible Jedhart axe of Sandy Armstrong. He clove a path amongst them as if he was cutting corn and those nearest him shrank back hampering those further back. The infuriated cattle still stampeding round the courtyard further impeded their efforts to halt him. In a few seconds he had reached the gap in the wall and leaped through it. Beyond the wall darkness was already falling and the mist was down over the moss.

"Follow me, who dares!" he shouted in triumph and disappeared into the gathering gloom.

Archie meanwhile withdrew into a niche in the passage behind the door as the besiegers burst into the house. Amongst them was one of the masked men carrying a torch in his hand. A desire for revenge fired the youngster and in an instant he had swung down his Jedhart axe in a sweeping blow which struck the torch from the invader's hand and three fingers with it. In the darkness which followed Archie slipped from his shelter and ran off into the courtyard, thinking to himself, "I've left my mark on that traitor and should know him again."

It did not take long for order to be restored in the ranks of the King's men. They soon had possession of Cleughfoot and remained there during the night. Archie and his mother were turned out of doors and forced to spend the night under guard in the bog. Then in the morning Cleughfoot was blown up in front of them and they were taken as prisoners to Sir William Selby who had his head-quarters at nearby Langholm.

"Who is this you are bringing before me?" demanded the knight. "A wife and a child! Have you been catching

131

sparrows and let the eagle fly free? Or have you the head and the hand of this Sandy Armstrong?"

"Indeed, Sir William," replied one of his officers. "His head remains where it should not be, still on his own shoulders. At the darkening he escaped into the bog. Three troopers guided by a masked man and a sleuth dog pursued him. When we crossed the bog this morning we found one of the troopers sunk to the middle in it and his horse beneath him and further on we found the dead bodies of the other two and the masked man and the sleuth dog all cleanly slain. I am sorry to have to report therefore that Sandy Armstrong has escaped, though we have reduced his stronghold to rubble and brought his wife and son, both Armstrongs indeed, to do with as you wish and may think proper."

"Tush, man," replied Sir William, the new-made knight. "Would you have us disgrace our royal commission by hanging women and children? Here, woman, away with you and take your brat with you and learn to live like honest folk. If you come my way again you will hang and that's an end of it. Begone!"

"And where shall we go, Archie?" she asked sorrowfully, as they withdrew from the knight's presence. "We have neither house, nor roof, friend nor kindred and who will shelter the wife and son of poor persecuted Sandy Armstrong?"

"Don't worry, mother," replied Archie, stoutly. "They may have burned Cleughfoot, but the stones are still left. I can soon build a place big enough for us to live in and while there's a hare on Tarras wood, or a sheep on the Leadhills, you shall never want, mother."

They returned sorrowfully to the heap of ruins which had been their home. Elspeth, in the bitterness of her spirit, sat down and wept desolately, but seeing her son busy about building a room she came to his help and within a couple of days they had built themselves a hut in the ruins which gave them some shelter from the elements. When that task was finished, however, she sank on her bed of rushes. It was clear that the will to live had left her and that the sickness of death was on her. She lay seemingly lifeless and almost speechless in a feverish coma.

"Oh, speak to me, mother!" cried young Archie. "What can I do for you?"

"Nothing, my son, nothing," groaned the dying woman. "The time is coming soon for Elspeth Armstrong, but may the saints in heaven protect my poor Archie."

She muttered a prayer to herself, but religion was not a strong point in the reiver's house, where the eighth commandment had been so little understood. Poor Archie sobbed aloud, unable to see where he could help.

"Oh, mother, mother, do not die!" he exclaimed.

He ran from the building with a broken jug he had found in the ruins of the building and filled it with water from a nearby spring. He bathed her heated brow and helped her to sip some of the liquid, but it brought little relief to her.

"I'll get you bread to eat," he cried. "But, mother, do not die and leave me alone."

After making her as comfortable as possible, he hurried from the ruins and ran at his topmost speed across the morass of Tarras and over the moors beyond until he came to the nearest habitation, a house occupied by Ringan Scott dependants of the Buccleuch family. The families had never been friends, but young Archie thought nothing of that in the agony of the moment. He rushed into the house in an almost demented frame of mind.

"Give me some bread, for the Lord's sake!" he cried. "I need bread for my mother's dying."

"Let her die and may you all die," said Ringan's son, Dick, who stood by the fire with his arm in a sling. "You'll get no bread from us."

"I must! I shall!" replied Archie vehemently and, seizing a half loaf of coarse cake, which lay on the table, he rushed out of the house.

They chased him for a mile or so, but despair and affection gave him speed and he soon outdistanced them. Finally he arrived back at his wretched hut and entered breathlessly.

"Mother, I've brought you some bread," he cried. "Here it is."

His mother did not reply and he paused uncertainly.

"Mother, speak to me!" he cried. "See. I have brought you some bread to eat. Just eat it and you'll feel better."

But still she remained silent and he approached closer to her bedside.

"Are you asleep, mother?" he asked, taking her hand

He shook her gently but she did not stir and her hand and face were cold.

"Oh, mother, mother!" he cried and, turning, rushed grief-stricken from the hut.

For most of the night he roamed the moor weeping until his grief was replaced with a sort of leaden calm acceptance. Then at dawn he returned to the hut and again sat beside his dead mother's corpse. For a day and a night he sat and mourned by her body. Then he took the remains of an iron gate and dug a grave for her. Finally he lifted her body and carried it in his arms, weeping again softly, and laid it in the grave he had prepared. He covered it with moss and green sod and for the rest of the day toiled hard rolling large stones from the ruins of his father's house to make a tall cairn over his mother's grave.

He had barely finished building this monument to his dead mother when a party of horsemen searching for his father rode up and asked him what he was doing. He explained what he had been about and in the bitterness of the moment accused them of being the murderers of both his father and his mother. In bitter tones he poured out his scorn on men who called themselves soldiers and killed women without pity or compassion.

Amongst the party was one of the principal leaders of the Elliot clan, who held land in the neighbourhood. He could not help feeling compassion for young Archie, as well as admiring the spirit of the lad so recently orphaned. He told him to come with him and promised to provide for him. Archie reluctantly obeyed and was employed by his protector to act as assistant to the shepherd in the hills.

Eighteen years passed and young Archie had learned to read and write. By this time he was the principal herdsman to his benefactor and was as widely liked and admired as his father had been feared. Yet there were times when his father's reiving spirit broke out and Archie had never forgiven the traitors, or as he termed them, the murderers of his parents.

Prominent amongst these was 'Fingerless Dick', as he was now generally known, the eldest son of Ringan Scott. Archie had long realised that he and his father must have been amongst the traitors who had led Selby's horsemen to Cleughfoot and shown the way over Tarras Moss. He also knew well that he must be the one whose fingers he had chopped off with his Jedhart axe on that fatal night.

That particular year there was a famous football match held in Liddesdale which all the Borderers had flocked to from many miles around. Amongst them was Archie's old enemy 'Fingerless Dick'. He jeered at Archie when he saw him and passed an unforgivable insult about his dead mother. Archie's blood was not slow to rise and hot words were soon exchanged. They grappled and wrestled with each other. They fell with Scott underneath and he drew his knife and thrust it into Archie's side. He was about to repeat the blow when Archie seized it from him and in the fury of the fight thrust it into Scott's chest. It seemed as if the thrust had killed him and some of Fingerless Dick's friends made an attempt to seize Archie, but he would have none of it. Wrenching a stave from one of them he brandished it in the air.

"Lay your hands on me at your peril!" he cried and, turning on his heels, bounded away at a speed that none of them could match.

Archie knew well enough that, although his enemy might recover, the Scotts would be only too eager to let loose the forces of the law on his head. Instead of returning to his master's house he sought safety in flight. Three days after the affray in Liddesdale, he entered Dumfries. He was travel-worn and weary for he had been running from glen to glen and staying on the open hillsides in case of pursuit.

Enquiring for a cheap lodging, he was shown to a small house near the foot of a street leading down to the river. It was filled with a motley group of beggars and pedlars and amongst the former was an old white-haired man of unusually large build. His white hair hung in still profuse locks down to his shoulders and his luxuriant beard, of similar snowy colour, descended to his chest. He wore an old grey cloak, gathered at the waist by a piece of rope instead of a girdle, and he had a patch over one eye. Something military in his bearing made it seem he might have been a soldier returned from the wars. He spoke little but his one eye was alert and a piercing blue, which often seemed to be fixed with interest in Archie's direction.

In the morning when Archie rose to leave, the old man accosted him.

"Where are you heading for, young man?" the elderly beggar enquired earnestly. "Are you for the north or the south?"

"What do you want to know for, old man?" enquired Archie cautiously.

"I have a good reason and it's one that cannot do you any harm," replied the old man. "If you can just put up with an old man's company for a little way I can promise you I will not be any trouble to you."

Archie saw no harm in agreeing to this and they set off together on the road towards Annan. It was a glorious sunny morning with the Solway on their left looking like a silver lake and not a cloud to be seen in the sky. For about three miles or so they went on their way in silence, although the old man sighed occasionally as if his mind was troubled.

"Let us just stop here and rest for a few moments," he suggested and sat himself down on a green tussock of grass by the wayside.

"Young man," he said, gazing steadfastly into Archie's face. "Your face reminds me strongly of someone I know.

Persecuted though the name is, answer me truly, is your name Armstrong?"

"It is," replied Archie stoutly. "And may the son of Sandy Armstrong perish the day he disowns it!"

"And your father and mother," continued the old man, hesitating as he spoke, "do they, does she, still live?"

Very briefly Archie described his father's persecution, of how he had been hunted from the country like a wild beast, of the destruction of his childhood home, and of his mother's death and her burial by his own hands in the wilds of Tarras Moss.

"Oh, my poor Elspeth!" cried the old man. "Archie, my son! My son! I am your father, Sandy Armstrong, returned at last."

"Father, my father!" exclaimed Archie embracing the old man in his arms.

When they had recovered themselves sufficiently the old man looked again at his son with renewed pleasure.

"Let us go no further south," he suggested. "But let us return to Tarras Moss and Cleughfoot, so that when my time comes you may lay me in peace alongside my Elspeth."

With a sad heart Archie told his father how he was flying from the grip of the law and the vengeance of the Scotts.

"Give them gold as a peace offering and buy them off," replied the old man contemptuously. "Ringan Scott and his like could never resist the lure of gold and they'll not have changed with the years."

From under his coarse cloak he pulled a leather purse filled to the neck with gold and placed it triumphantly in his son's hands. For nearly twenty years after leaving his native soil and reaching the continent safely, Sandy had served in foreign wars as a mercenary and with his outstanding strength and valour had attained rank, honour and riches. On returning to his native land he had decided to assume the disguise of a beggar in order to make sure that it was quite safe for him to return and to make certain he would no longer be liable to prosecution for his old reiving offences. His primary concern, however, as he explained to

137

Archie, was to learn what news there was of his wife and son and see what he could do to make amends for deserting them.

Together father and son returned to Tarras side in triumph. As Sandy had expected, the sight of a few gold coins was enough to make Fingerless Dick drop any attempt at prosecution. With the backing of his father's gold Archie was able to set up as a sheep farmer himself and married his former employer's daughter. At the age of four score years and ten the old reiver Sandy Armstrong finally died peacefully in his son's house on Tarras Moor surrounded by his grandchildren. According to his wishes, he was laid to rest alongside his wife Elspeth in the wildness of the moor where two twin cairns now mark their final resting place.

Unfortunately much of this wild and desolate Border countryside has been deep ploughed and drained and is now under regiments of dark green conifers which have totally changed the character of the area. Not so Tarras Moss, east of Langholm, which remains wild and desolate and, like most of this area, a part of the Buccleuch estates. It is now a grouse moor and the most war-like sounds to be heard there today are the popping of the guns in August and September. For the rest of the year the curlews, grouse and blackgame have the area to themselves with a few sheep for company. Sandy Armstrong and his wife Elspeth are not likely to be disturbed.

Some five miles south of Tarras Moss is the village of Canonbie which makes a useful base for exploring this area. South of Canonbie was an area always known as the "Debatable Land" since it could never be decided whether it was owned by the Scots or the English.

Langholm, a pleasant, small textile town, to the west of Tarras Moss, is also a useful centre for exploring the Middle March, down into Cumbria or north into Liddesdale.

WILL ARMSTRONG AND
THE LURDON

By the reign of Charles I the Borders were beginning to feel the rule of law more firmly at last. Reiving on any scale was becoming a thing of the past, although the Borderers themselves, as already indicated, were always ready to turn to alternative ways of making a living and were as ready to steal a cow as kidnap a young girl, or as in this case a judge. This tale is based on actual events that took place more or less as described. The President of the Court of Session in Edinburgh was indeed kidnapped and kept a prisoner for some months. Belief in witchcraft was very strong both in England and in Scotland at this time. The Reformation might have begun to take effect, but in a climate of religious intolerance bigotry inevitably flourished.

IN THE early days of Charles I the Borders were beginning to feel the power of the law at last. The old ways were beginning to be met with resolute condemnation. The Wardens of the Marches on both sides of the Border were taking firm steps to control the outlaws who still tried to live by the old ways of border reiving. The chances of anyone taken in the act of stealing cattle surviving to tell the tale were few indeed for the powers that be were determined to stamp out the constant cattle rustling and sheep stealing which those who held to the older ways felt was the natural life for the Borderer.

Prominent amongst the remaining reivers was Will Armstrong of Gilnockie Tower, a descendant of the famed Johnny Armstrong who, having been enticed into the presence of King James V with the promise of a safe conduct, was then hung at Carlenrig with twenty-five of his followers. According to the ballad, he was reputed to have declaimed proudly on the scaffold: "I haif asked grace at a graceless face, but there is nane for my men and me." Despite this, his tower at Gilnockie does not seem to have been forfeited to the Crown.

Will Armstrong was six-foot-five inches tall, broad of shoulder and as handsome a man as any in the Borders, powerful and fleet of foot. On horseback and with a sword in his hand, or hand to hand, there were few who could begin to hold their own against him. He was both bold and dashing and had a keen sense of humour. In short he was a worthy descendant of his famous forebear and only unfortunate to live in a period when the old ways were no longer being treated as tolerantly as in the past. Yet his wife, Margaret Elliot, was a woman who held strongly to the old ways and felt the world was falling apart whenever they were forced to dine on their own cattle or sheep.

For most of their married life Will Armstrong had successfully adhered to the old dictums of 'conveying' – the polite term then used for change of ownership, which was by no means confined to cattle and sheep. As the old ballad had it:

> They left not spindell, spoone nor speit,
> Bed, bolster, blanket, sark, nor sheet.

Will's own feelings on the subject he made plain enough: "To steal cattle or drive a score of sheep homewards is nothing very special," he declared. "But to steal a *Lord*, now there's something worthy of a man's genius and only fit for an Armstrong to execute."

No doubt, when he was making this idle boast, Will little thought that he would ever have to live up to his words. The day was to come, however, when not only did he have to make them good, but his own life depended on his success, for inevitably Will was caught out in his misdeeds. His wife had been urging him for some time to go out and find some meat for the house. Will had reminded her that the Jedburgh Justice was doling out heavy penalties for lesser crimes, but finally he had given way. Thereupon he had been apprehended by a pure mischance, surrounded by a score of followers of the Lord Justice General just as he was making off with the cow of a farmer named Grant at Stobs. He was taken back at once to Jedburgh gaol where things promised to go badly for him at the next sitting of the court.

The capture made a great stir in Liddesdale. All those who had been his victims at various times raised a cheer and all those who like him were more inclined to regard others' cattle as their own were greatly perturbed at this evidence of the government's apparent determination to prove that 'might is right'. No-one was more put out than Margaret Elliot, his wife, who felt, not without reason, that she had a good deal of responsibility for what had happened. At first she sobbed and cried bitterly, making so much noise that the ravens and the owls in Gilnockie Tower rose up in alarm and deserted the building. Then abruptly she pulled herself together.

"What are you about, woman?" she demanded. "Shall Will Armstrong, the bravest man in the Borders, be hanged because a cow that knew no better followed him from Stobs to the Hollows? And shall it be said that Margaret Elliot was the death of her own brave man? I had meat enough in the larder that day I scorned him with his laziness and forced him to go out to do the deed that has landed him in Jedburgh gaol. But I'll away to the Warden, James Stewart of Traquair, and see if it really should be the King's will that a man's life be forfeit for a cow's."

Making good her resolution she threw her plaid over her shoulders and set off for Traquair House, which still stands with its high white walls, crow-stepped gables and gothic windows, at the edge of the Tweed. Arriving at the front door she made her presence known.

"Is my Lord Steward at home?" she asked the servant who answered the door.

"He is," the man replied. "And who is it who wishes to see him?"

"The Mistress of Gilnockie," she replied proudly, "has come to seek a good word for Will Armstrong who now lies in Jedburgh gaol for stealing a tether and I fear may even hang for it."

The servant listened to this extraordinary message with due attention and gravity, but declared severely that he could not deliver such a message to his lordship.

"I am not asking you to deliver the message, my man," replied Margaret stoutly. "I merely wished to be polite to you and show you a little attention. God be thanked the Mistress of Gilnockie can deliver her own messages."

With that she pushed the man aside with a thrust of her brawny arm and calmly went forward to the door of the main room inside, which she intended to open. By this time the manservant was at her heels and, seizing her plaid, was in the act of pulling her backwards when the door opened and the Warden himself appeared to demand the cause of the unseemly noise.

"Is this house yours, my Lord, or is it this man's?" asked Margaret. "Take my advice, my Lord, and turn him off. Would you believe it, my Lord, though he's employed for the purpose of letting folk in to see your Lordship, he actually – aye as sure as death – tried to keep me out. Can you deny it, man? Look in my face and deny it if you dare."

The manservant could not help smiling and Lord Traquair laughed outright at this naïve approach. Margaret herself wondered greatly at the good nature of his Lordship in forgiving such an offence so readily.

"Well, if you're as forgiving to me as you are to yon fellow," she went on, as she followed him into his room, "Will Armstrong will not hang."

"What's this?" demanded the Warden. "What is it that you want, my good woman?"

"As if your Lordship didn't know," answered Margaret, with a knowing look. "Is it likely that a Liddesdale woman from the Hollows should call upon the Warden for anything short of the life and safety of the man who's in Jedburgh gaol?"

"I'm still at a loss, my good woman," said the Warden.

"At a loss!" rejoined Margaret. "What! Doesn't the whole of Ettrick Forest and Teviotdale and Tweeddale know that Will Armstrong's in Jedburgh gaol!"

"I know well, good woman, that the brave reiver is in prison," replied the Warden. "But I thought his crime was the theft of a cow and not a tether as I heard you say to my servant."

"Well, well now – the cow may have been at the end of the tether," replied Margaret.

"She is a wise woman who concealeth the *extremity* of her husband's crime," replied Lord Traquair, with a smile. "But what would you have me do?"

"Just save Will Armstrong from the gallows, my Lord," replied Margaret.

Then lowering her voice and going close to the Warden she went on confidentially.

"Sometimes a lord needs a hand as much as the next man. If there's no deer on Traquair when your Lordship has company at the castle you have only to say the word to Will and there will be no want of venison here for a month. And there's not a reiver in Liddesdale, be he baron or bondsman, knight or knave, but Will can bring him to you at your Lordship's command, with a week's warning." Then she added in very confidential tones, "And if your Lordship was needing a bonnie lady to keep the Traquair House in order I daresay my Will could find you whatever one you had in mind and bring her to you unscathed sooner than a priest could tie the knot. Is such a man to be hanged for a paltry cow, my Lord?"

"By my faith, your husband has some unusual qualifica-

143

tions to him," replied Traquair. "There is certainly no one in these parts but knows Will Armstrong, or of him, but I am afraid it is just because of that fact that he is in danger of hanging. He is the last of the old Armstrongs and you must know the saying:

'Come Liddesdale's peace, when Armstrongs cease.'

"It would not look well for the King's Warden to let the noose slip which will provide peace and order in the land. Yet Will is too fine a fellow to hang. Go on your way and leave it to me. I'll see to him."

"Oh, no, my Lord," replied Margaret firmly. "I'll not move from this house until you say you'll save him this one time. I'll stand caution and surety for him myself that he'll never again dine in Gilnockie Tower on another man's sirloins. His clan has long been broken, but I now stand as head of it and it has always been the custom of the country to make the head answer for the rest of the body."

"Well, that is also the custom of the hangman at Jedburgh," answered Traquair with a laugh. "But go on home with you. Will Armstrong will not hang yet. I have a task for him to do for me. I have a lurdon of the north he must steal for me. I'll give you my word."

A 'lurdon' was the vernacular term for an old wife and although the news surprised Margaret Elliot she was in no mood to enquire too deeply of the Warden's intentions just so long as he stood by his word.

"Give me your hand then, my Lord," she replied, determined to seal the bargain. "He'll bring the richest lurdon in the land to your Lordship, as surely as he ever took a Cumberland cow, which as your Lordship knows is not reiving. Just you let him know about it and the deed's as good as done."

Traquair gave the doughty wife his hand and she departed wondering what the Warden could want with a stolen lurdon. A young woman might have been a fair prize for the handsome baron, but an old wife was the most extraordinary object of reiving she had ever heard suggested.

144

The next day Traquair mounted his horse and set off for Jedburgh. Once there he went immediately to the gaol. Margaret, however, had already been before him to let her husband know that the Warden was soon to visit him to get him released, on condition that he stole a lurdon from the north. The unusual nature of this request appeared to both of them much greater than the difficulty, unless, as Will had suggested, she was bedridden, in which case it would be no easy task to convey her, since horses were the only means of transport at the time. But the problem of why on earth the Warden should want an old wife was beyond their wildest conjectures. But come what may Will Armstrong resolved that he would do the Warden's bidding and so regain his freedom.

This was the state of affairs when the gaoler opened the door of his cell and announced the arrival of the Warden.

"You'll have to hang this time, Will," said the Warden, adopting as gruff a tone as he could, as he stepped over the threshold. "It's not in the power of man to save you now."

"Begging your Lordship's pardon," replied Will. "That's as may be, but I believe it to be in the power of a woman. The old lurdon will be at Traquair whenever your Lordship decrees."

"And who is the old lurdon?" asked the Warden, with a smile which he could not repress.

"Ah, my Margaret couldn't tell me that," replied Will. "But it's just for your Lordship to tell me who she is and for me to steal the old lady away as surely as I ever conveyed an old milker from over the border. I'm no sooner free than she's yours."

The familiar way in which Will Armstrong spoke of the female to be kidnapped made the Warden laugh outright in a manner Will found not altogether consistent with the serious nature of the subject.

"Where is she, my Lord?" asked Will. "Where am I to take her and how long must she be a prisoner?"

"I am afraid, Will, she's beyond the power of man," the Warden replied in serious tones. "But on condition of your

145

making a fair shot at it I will see your life is saved and take my chance on your success. A lot depends on you suc-ceeding. My own barony of Coberston depends on this par-ticular lurdon being held for three months in a quiet corner of Graeme's Tower. Do you know the place?"

"Ah, yes, I know it well," replied Will, who began to see the importance of his mission, but was now immensely curious as to the identity of the old wife. "But who is she, my Lord?"

"It is you who have said she is a woman," replied the Warden with a smile. "And I have not corrected you. Have you ever heard, Will, of fifteen old women, 'lurdons' as they are widely known, who reside in a large house in Parliament Close in Edinburgh?"

"Ah, well enough," replied Will with a grim smile of understanding. "And well I know the old wives. Anyone that has a character to lose or a property to keep against the claims of old parchment knows those fifteen old wives. No-one's character is safe from them. Why, they even suggested my Tower of Gilnockie should be forfeit to the King! No doubt they are behind any danger to your fine barony of Coberston, but what exactly do you want me to do?"

"Well, Will, they're securely locked up in their strong Parliament House and the question is how to get at them," replied Traquair.

"From what you say I fancy just one of the lurdons will satisfy your lordship," replied Will. "Or do you want me to take all fifteen to lodge in Graeme's Tower? A fine nest of screech owls they'd make lodged there."

"I will indeed be content with just one of them," agreed the Warden.

"Ah well, now I see it," replied Will. "One of the old wives has been undermining Coberston, is that it? What is her name, my Lord?"

"Gibson of Durie," replied Traquair.

"Ah so," said Will. "The oldest of the fifteen, if I'm not mistaken. Lady President of the bunch. She was against me when the question of Gilnockie Tower came up so I owe her

146

a score. How long do you want her lodged in Graeme's Tower?"

"Three months should be enough to change matters," replied the Warden. "But it seems a desperate enterprise to ask of any man, Will."

"Desperate, my Lord?" replied Will with a laugh. "The word's not known in the Borders."

"Well, the consequences for you could be great, Will," said Traquair. "You are in gaol here for stealing a cow and would be hanged for it if I did not set you free. Our laws are equal and humane. For stealing a cow you may be hanged, but there's no such law against stealing a judge."

"That shows the good sense of the lawyers for once," replied Will with a leer. "The legislature has wisely weighed the merits of the two. Yet if it were not for your case, my Lord, I could wish the law reversed. I would be in no hurry to steal one of these creatures, at least for my own use; and as for my wife, she'd rather see a cow at Gilnockie any day."

"Well, Will," said the Warden. "I am not asking you to steal old Lady Gibson for me. I dare not do so. You understand me? But I am saving your life and I can tell you if that big-wigged person is not lodged inside Graeme's Tower within ten days my estate at Coberston will have a new owner and your benefactor will be a lordly beggar."

"Fear not, my Lord," replied Will. "I'm no sooner out than she's in. She'll not have a word to say against Coberston for the next three months, I'll promise you."

Having put his case to him and being assured of his promise to at least attempt what seemed the impossible, the Warden departed. Two days later Will was released. On his return to Gilnockie, however, he did not reveal to his wife who the old lurdon was that the Warden wanted him to capture, for the Warden had more than hinted that this would be unwise. Instead he settled down with two friends who had often helped him in reiving expeditions and for several hours they discussed their plans.

As a result of their discussions the three were soon mounted on their stout Galloway ponies and heading off

147

for Edinburgh, with a fourth led by the bridle and carrying provisions for several days as well as a large cloak and several other articles. Taking the least frequented road to Edinburgh they put their horses up at a small inn in the Grassmarket.

The next day Will found his way to Parliament House and sat himself down in one of the litigants' benches facing the fifteen law-lords who were sitting in a half-circle robed and bewigged as they decided the cases brought before them. He understood little of the proceedings as the advocates held forth in front of their Lordships, but he kept his eyes fixed on the face of the President, Lord Gibson of Durie.

Halfway through the day he heard the case announced: "Maxwell against Lord Traquair." Then he heard Lord Gibson, the President, speak.

"This case I believe involved the right of the large barony of Coberston. Seven of my brethren, you are aware, have given their opinions in favour of the defendant Lord Traquair and seven for the pursuer Maxwell. My casting vote must therefore decide the case, but there are still some difficulties I cannot surmount."

"Aha. And there's a new one sitting in front of you," thought Will Armstrong on hearing these words. "And maybe the worst of them all."

"I still require some confirmation before I pronounce judgment in the case. I am sorry that my learned friends at the bar have not relieved me of my scruples."

"Stupid idiots, they are," thought Will. "But don't you worry, my Lord Durie. I'll relieve you of them, believe you me."

The case being the last of the day, the court was then adjourned and the judges retired to remove their wigs and gowns. Will, never at a loss, enquired of an attendant where he might see the judges leave the court as he was curious as a simple countryman to see for himself what they looked like without their regalia and in their everyday clothes. The seemingly simple request was soon gratified and Will

148

stationed himself at the door indicated, watching as their Lordships one by one departed.

When he saw the face of the President appear he was gratified to find that the figure now revealed was no longer that of an apparently portly figure but rather a thin and spare individual who, to his Borderer's eye, was eminently portable and suitable for conveying as required. Following the judge as he made his way homewards, Will Armstrong observed him return to his house in the Canongate. He took careful note of the house and decided that his next object was to find out if and when he took an evening stroll.

With his friends he set a watch on the house and on the first evening they were disappointed to find that the President never set foot outside his household. On the other hand he was able during this period to work out a plan whereby one of his friends kept the horses available at the foot of the Leith Wynd while he placed himself so as to cover either end of the passage where the President's house stood. His other friend he stationed as go-between in case of trouble. A series of whistles was agreed as signals when required.

The second evening, two hours after the learned judge had left Parliament House, a whistle from Will's friend indicated that he had seen the President leaving his house. Will recognised him at once and sent his friend to warn the horseholder to be ready for action. He then followed the judge as he walked along clearly deeply involved in his own thoughts.

Will was sure that he was contemplating the seizure of Coberston from his benefactor Traquair and his resolve was such that he was hard put to it not to seize the President in the street in full view of the populace. However he was delighted to find that in search of solitude to allow his thoughts free rein Lord Gibson turned away into a narrow alleyway and thence to a quiet area called the Figgate Whins.

He was strolling there with no-one in sight and barely a sound to break his meditations when suddenly he was seized

149

from behind and a cloak thrown over his head enveloping him completely. His arms were bound fast to his sides and his legs likewise and then his body thrust face down over a horse. A few turns more of the cord and he was off at a hard gallop, barely aware of what had happened to him, fastened securely to the garron like a piece of baggage.

This was a period when witchcraft was not only widely believed in but was frequently a matter before the courts. The Lord Justice himself had many times had occasion to hear trials for sorcery and condemn the witches before him to being pricked and burned. Like most of his fellows he believed fervently in the black arts and the power of witches. His first thoughts, having seen no-one and having suddenly apparently been enveloped in a black bag and then sub-jected to a wild ride, was that he had been seized by witches and was about to be condemned by them to the same fate that he had condemned many of their fellows.

Whenever the travellers were obliged to slow down or even halt to ask the way on the outskirts of the city, they explained they were conveying a particularly sinful old witch down to Dumfries to be burned. The half-suffocated and speechless judge rendered more than half-senseless by the proceedings occasionally heard shouts which con-firmed his belief that he was in the hands of sorcerers or witches.

"See the old witch is well pricked and then burned in flaming tar," shouted one man, prodding the wretched judge with his stave.

"Away with the old witch, duck her well and see if she floats," cried another.

Hearing these occasional shouts, but otherwise not a word, for his kidnappers rode for the most part in total silence, the judge had no way of guessing where he was travelling to or how far he had gone. It seemed to him, how-ever, that he was undoubtedly in the power of sorcerers and doomed soon to die. One or two fear-stricken cries that he made early on revealed to the astute Will the way his mind was working and the reiver determined to work on his fears.

150

As soon as they were on the road to Moffat and safe from any pursuit they slackened pace slightly, but still kept up a steady enough trot. Any conversation taking place within hearing of the wretched judge, lashed as he was to the back of the garron, concerned his likely fate and kept him in a state of fearful tension. Subjected to continual jolting and total darkness, half suffocated and for the most part barely half-conscious, after a while the wretched Lord Gibson was in no state to protest or do more than sink into a state of frightened lethargy.

The reivers may have slowed their pace, but their powerful little garrons did not halt. Accustomed as they were to lengthy rides, those horses had their fill. Throughout the night and most of the next day the reivers and their 'lurdon' kept a steady pace, merely slowing occasionally and only halting very briefly to allow the horses water and a quick bite of oats.

Towards the evening of the next day they approached the isolated Graeme's Tower, on the Dryfe Water, not very far beyond Moffat. In a deep cell, far underground, the President of the Court of Session was unrolled from the cloak in total darkness and his bonds severed. The door was then closed and the reivers retreated. Food and water was brought to him daily and fed to him through a small grating through which he also obtained what little light was available. Freed though he was, the bewildered judge had never seen his captors and never saw who brought him the small daily rations on which he managed to survive. With no other explanation available he was still convinced that he must have been spirited into captivity by evil spirits.

As soon as the reiver had shut the door on his prisoner he sat down and wrote a brief, but explicit message to his benefactor – "The cat's in the bag" – and sent it by one of his friends to Traquair.

The moment it arrived the Earl of Traquair read the message and laughed at its brevity. A few days later he set off for Edinburgh, which he found still in a state of surprise at the sudden and unexplained disappearance of the

President of the Court of Session. There had been a hue and cry and widespread searches for any sign of him. Rewards had been offered for any explanation as to his disappearance, but all to no avail. The general conclusion was that he must have wandered down to the sands of Leith where the incoming tide encroaches on the shore with great speed and had often been known to overtake those who had ventured too far out.

The coast as far as Musselburgh and Cramond had been scoured in search of his body but to no avail. After a month it was decided that he must have drowned, even though no body was to be found. Lady Gibson and her family went into mourning. His colleagues on the Court of Session lamented his passing and duly elected another member in his place.

On the election of a new President more favourable to his case the Earl of Traquair again raised the question of a judgment in the issue. He claimed that with fourteen judges equally divided he was now entitled as defender to a decision in his favour. This approach was not accepted, but the new President was in favour of his side of the case and he did not expect to be kept waiting much longer for a positive decision.

Meanwhile the wretched Lord President of the Court was still the victim of his own superstitious fears. Confined in the underground cell as he was, with only a faint light coming through the grill and with unseen hands delivering food and water once a day, he was still convinced that he was being held by demons or sorcerers determined to have their way with him. Throughout his lengthy confinement he came close to losing his reason and it is not surprising that he became prey to all sorts of strange fancies and dreads.

The only sounds he could hear during the day were a man's voice sometimes calling loudly, "Batty, Batty", or towards evening a woman's voice calling, "Madge, Madge". These were in fact the voices of a shepherd calling his dog each morning to round up the sheep and an old woman living in a nearby cottage calling her cat in at night. So regular were these cries and sometimes so persistent that,

152

being still convinced he was in the power of sorcerers, he came to the conclusion that there must be two demons named Batty and Madge who were expressly waiting to torment him. Daily he prayed fervently that he might be delivered from these dreadful demons.

Finally the day came when Lord Traquair's case was heard again and this time the successor to Lord Gibson as President gave the deciding vote for the Warden. As soon as he was sure that he had secured his case and that his estate was once again safely his, Traquair sent a messenger to Will Armstrong with a note as brief as the one he had received.

"Let the cat out of the bag," he wrote.

Will and his friends then set about releasing their wretched prisoner in a manner somewhat similar to his capture. The first their victim knew of their presence the door of his cell had opened and he was once again muffled in a black cloak and bound securely. He was then bundled on horseback. The three rode round and round Graeme's Tower at a gallop for several hours, so that the bewildered man had no idea of how far he had travelled. Finally he was set down at his starting point and laid on the ground with the ropes loosened, whereupon they mounted their horses and set off home to Gilnockie Tower.

The wretched Lord President of the Court of Session, a bedraggled and grey-bearded figure, gaunt and fearful, saw the sun rise for the first time in three months and went down on his knees in gratitude for being delivered from the evil attentions of the twin devils, Batty and Madge, whom he was convinced had been keeping him prisoner. He had barely risen to his feet when he heard a cry nearby of "Batty, Batty". A moment later this was followed by a cry of "Madge, Madge". Both these were exactly as he had heard them for the past three months.

Turning round he saw a shepherd calling his dog and an old woman in a cottage doorway calling her cat, both animals responding to their names. He could not believe his eyes, for it seemed to him he had ridden on horseback many miles and yet here were these very names being shouted in front of him with the demons possibly taking the shape of these ordinary looking animals.

"Good morning, old man, and where have you come from?" asked the shepherd, in surprised tones. "You must have travelled far in the night to be here so early."

"Would you care to come in and rest?" enquired the old woman hospitably.

But Lord Gibson was sure these were demons sent to plague him and that they had changed their outward shape into animal form. He gazed dumbly in horror at the simple shepherd and the old lady with their dog and cat. He himself made such a strange figure, with the cloak still hanging over his head and down his back and his eyes rolling speechlessly in his gaunt face, that the old lady, who was fearful of the ghosts said to haunt the nearby tower, was convinced he must be a sorcerer.

"Avaunt ye!" she cried. "Avaunt ye, evil spirit."

"Aye, avaunt," cried the shepherd, joining her condemnation.

It was too much for Lord Gibson and, throwing down the cloak, he set off as fast as he could run on his weakened legs until he was exhausted. Some hours later, following a track over the hills, he came to a farmhouse where he was greeted hospitably and fed. Since he insisted on asking not only the day and the month but also the year, they put him down as simple-minded and, as he had no money on him, treated him in a kindly manner as a passing beggar.

In this way begging from farmhouse to farmhouse and hamlet to hamlet, he gradually made his way back to Edinburgh, but since he kept trying to find out what year it was everyone tended to regard him as half-witted. On the one occasion he attempted to reveal his name and rank he learned that Lord Gibson of Durie had been drowned in the Forth and after that he made no further attempt to explain who he was. Since he had no explanation himself for where he had been, the journey was something of a nightmare to him, the more especially as he was unaware if his wife had re-married during his absence.

Eventually he reached the outskirts of Edinburgh, foot-sore, weary and looking like a gaunt shadow of his former self. The sight of Arthur's Seat and the familiar cloud of smoke known to everyone in Edinburgh and its surrounds as "Auld Reekie putting on her nightcap", when all the inhabitants stoked up their fires for the evening meal, quickened his pace. Soon he was close to his old, familiar surroundings and several people whom he knew passed him in the street, but although he waved at them they with one accord stared at him, appearing not to recognise him, or hurried on their way.

Finally he encountered one of his fellow judges, Lord Farquhar, who had sat next to him on the bench for many years. By this time the light was fading towards evening and without thinking of his appearance, so overjoyed was he to see someone he knew and who knew him at last, that he rushed up to him with his hand outstretched, his teeth bared in his gaunt and pallid face in a smile of joy. His old friend took one terrified look at him and instead of returning his greeting turned around and fled as if all the demons of hell were behind him.

Shaken and somewhat discouraged by this reaction, he quickened his steps towards the Canongate, but by the time he reached his old home darkness had fallen. He peered through the window and saw his wife still in her widow's mourning black, with their children also wearing mourning bands. The sight was too much for him and, forgetful of his appearance, he thrust open the door and rushed into the room. His wife promptly screamed and fell into a faint. The children also screamed and some rushed out of the room. The servants appeared in the doorway and they too screamed at the sight of Lord Gibson's gaunt spectre returning to haunt his old home.

Little by little order was restored and by speaking softly to his wife Lord Gibson eventually convinced her that it was indeed her husband returned from the dead, having been spirited away and imprisoned by evil demons. The servants were persuaded to put a meal in front of him and by the

155

hearty appetite he showed all were soon convinced that Lord Gibson, the late President of the Court of Session, had indeed returned from the dead.

Although he returned to take his place in the Court of Session Lord Gibson of Durie was never quite the same man again. His condemnation of witches and his sentences in such cases were notable for their strength of feeling. The case of Lord Traquair's rights in his estate was not one that ever arose again and the Warden was well content with Will Armstrong's remarkable conveyance. The Borderer himself remained a more or less reformed character, for his wife was wise enough never to urge him on to convey his neighbour's cattle again. At any rate, with the backing of the Warden as his benefactor, Will Armstrong never again landed in Jedburgh gaol, even if the odd sheep may have vanished mysteriously during the moonlight nights from Cumbria and places south.

The rocky promontory above the River Esk on which Gilnockie Tower was sited is some four miles south-east of Langholm, but the stones of the tower where John Armstrong and subsequently his descendant, Will, lived have been used to build the nearby Gilnockie Bridge over the River Esk.

Traquair House, about a mile south of Innerleithen, still remains in good order, open to the public and well worth a visit.

As noted already, Langholm makes a good base for touring this area. To savour the Border character to the full it is worth attending some of the Common Ridings, held regularly each year by any Border town worthy of the name, when the bounds of the town are ridden by a company on horseback. Langholm Common Riding is a particularly splendid celebration, but be warned the town and surrounding area is fully booked for months in advance by expatriate sons and daughters returning for the event.

THE FAAS' REVENGE

Throughout their turbulent history the Borderers had naturally grown to know each other, as well as each other's country, well. They were also, quite naturally, very much inter-related. There were Armstrongs and Johnstones, Maxwells and Scotts, to name but a few, to be found on both sides of the Borders. It was not uncommon when Borderers met in armed conflict for cousins to recognise each other while exchanging blows and even to enquire after mutual blood relations. In Cumbria and in Northumberland the same attitudes to reiving and raiding had long been shared from sheer necessity. With the Union of the Crowns, however, here too a greater respect for the law prevailed.

Common to both sides of the border at this period were the various clans of gypsies and tinkers, who were to be seen regularly touring the countryside or camping in secluded copses, making their living off the land as itinerant beggars and thieves. Often to be seen at fairs and markets, they were generally disliked, but accepted as a natural enough part of the life of the day. Rival gangs, or tribes, often met in pitched battle and since the men were frequently aggressive and ready with their knives, they were treated with some respect, amounting to fear, by outlying farmsteads. They were never above stealing fowls, sheep, or for that matter horses. A child taken now and then as a convenient slave, or in revenge for some slight, was not out of the way. Stories of such events are sufficiently common to have undoubted basis in fact. The Faa were certainly a real gypsy tribe who had a base of sorts in or around Yetholm and the story appears to be based on truth.

IN THE early sixteenth century, during the reign of James VI, a notorious tribe of gypsies named Faa first came to Scotland. The name was said to be derived from Farr, or Fall, but be that as it may, they soon established themselves in the Border country, ranging far and wide. Since their travelling bands often attracted hangers-on and dependants, who were not strictly members of the original family, they tended to form quite large gangs. No peaceable householder, or even estate owner, would generally wish to pick a quarrel with them, for their memories were long and poultry or sheep were likely to vanish and cattle or horses might be lamed, or die mysteriously, for years after the original event whenever they, or any of their followers, were in the district.

In 1628, on a dark and gale torn night in December, a Faa gang of gypsies requested refuge from the stormy night in the outhouses of the Laird of Clennel in the Upper Coquetdale in Northumberland. The laird himself was already in bed, but the domestic staff, being few in number, were frightened at the sight of a large Faa gang grouped at the front door and afraid to refuse such a seemingly modest request.

"You may have a shelter for the night," agreed Andrew Smith, who was the major domo of the household, though a man without any real authority or personality. "But I will trust on your honour not to allow any of your people to steal any poultry, sheep or cattle from the estate. If the laird knew that any of you had been staying here the night it would be as much as my life's worth. He was in a great rage about some of your people only recently."

"Tut, tut, man," replied Willie Faa, the king of the tribe. "You fear the death you'll never die. Willie Faa and his

158

people live as well as the Laird of Clennel. But here's my hand that not a four-footed beast, or a feather of a bird, shall be touched by me or mine. But I see the light is out in the laird's window. He is asleep and high up in the turrets, so why should you put human beings up in stables and cattle sheds on a night like this when your hall fire is still burning well and there is room enough for us all around it? Give us a seat by it and you will not be the loser. And I promise you that we shall be off, bag and baggage, before the break of day, and before the laird begins to wake."

For all the half-wheedling tones of the request, there was no mistaking the threat behind it. Furthermore while Andrew Smith had been speaking to King Willie, as he styled himself, the rest of the gang had sneaked in behind him. The few male servants and all the females were being solicited by various members of the gang to have their fortunes told, or were otherwise engaged in conversation. Some of them further urged Andrew Smith to reconsider his decision to banish the tribe to the outhouses and he saw that in the circumstances the request amounted to a command whether he liked it or not.

"But just think what a terrible row there would be if the laird was to waken, or get wind of such a thing," he protested feebly.

"Fear not your laird," said Elspeth, wife of the king and renowned as a fortune-teller. "I will lay a spell on him so that he cannot be roused from sleep until I, at sunrise, wash my hands in the Darden well.

The fortune-teller then raised her arms and waving them in the air uttered a simple incantation:

> *Oh, Queen of day and of the night,*
> *Keep Clennel's laird beneath your spell,*
> *Until the morn has dawned full bright,*
> *And I have washed in Darden Well.*

With his fears to some extent soothed by the impressive air with which this was uttered and in any event making the best of a bad job, Andrew ushered the Faas into the main hall for the night. There they seated themselves on oak forms round the fire in a large semi-circle.

"Now," said the Faa king, rubbing his hands together. "The night is cold, bitterly cold, Mr Smith. Although the fire is warm enough for the outer man, is there nothing in the cellar that will warm the inner man? Now, come, see to it!"

"R-r-r-really, sir," replied Andrew, stuttering as he spoke, despite his efforts to appear at ease. "I would give you just what I would take myself, but the liquor in the cellars is the laird's, not mine. Furthermore there's never so much to spare that he would fail to miss any. But there is some excellent cold beef in the pantry if you could put up with that and the home-brewed which we drink in the servant's hall."

"Andrew, my man," replied the Faa king proudly and with a clear underlying threat in his voice, "castles I have not, flocks and herds I have not, nor do I own fields where wheat, oats and barley grow, and like Ishmael, the outcast, my great forefather, every man's hand is against me and mine against them, but when I am hungry I do not lack the flesh-pots of my native land and the moor-fowl and the venison make a fine stew together. Cold meat does not sit well on my stomach and the King of the Faas does not drink the servants' brew. Do you follow me, Andrew?"

"Oh, I do, sir, I do," replied the major domo, reluctantly. "But, as I have said, sir, the drink is not mine to give. If I do bring you a jug I hope that will suffice and you'll not be wanting more."

"We shall try it," replied the royal gypsy in a grand manner.

With great reluctance, Andrew withdrew to the cellar and returned with a large jug of the best ale, which he placed on a table in the midst of them. The king of the Faas condescended to pronounce the ale drinkable and raised his mug to a better acquaintance with the Laird of Clennel's cellars. Meanwhile, as her husband and his followers sat carousing on the fine ale along with the male servants,

Elspeth sat amongst the maid servants examining the lines on the palms of their hands and pursuing her calling as a fortune-teller. Every now and then as she traced the lines of matrimony, or of fate, she would pause and exclaim in tones of desperation, "Ha, now, quickly, cross my palm again with silver, lass. I see fortune, gold and a spur, a sword, a shield and a crest. They are there as plain as a pikestaff, but cross my palm again for until the silver again crosses it I cannot see whether they are yours or not."

In this wheedling manner she continued to spin out the fortunes of the maid servants until their last coins were in her possession. From that she went on to demand their trinkets in place of silver to complete her outline of their future. Then, as they watched her solemn tones and convincing air, the male servants one by one also requested her to tell their fortunes. Finally even Andrew Smith's curiosity was sufficiently roused to make him approach her and ask her to glance at his hand to tell him what the future held for him.

She raised it and held it before her eyes.

"Ah, this is a dark and difficult hand," she muttered. "Here are ships and sea and a crossing of the sea, with danger and a way to avoid it and much gold at the end of it. But cross my hand again with silver, sir, for yours is a hard hand to see."

Soon Andrew had given her all the money in his possession and, like the others, was forced to turn to payment in kind. Although it was understood she would return the money and the trinkets when the fortunes were all told it was natural enough to feel a reluctance to part with favoured possessions. First went his favourite silver snuff-box.

"It won't do. I cannot see it yet," she groaned. "I cannot see beyond the danger that is to come to the gold you will gain thereafter. Cross my palm again, my man."

"That's all I have, I fear," he replied sadly.

"Not a bit of it!" she replied. "You have a pocket watch and chain there, I see, which tells you the minutes now. It may well help me to show you those to come."

161

Reluctantly, and after a good deal of hesitation, Andrew handed over his watch and chain. They disappeared immediately into a convenient bag which already held all the offerings made to her. At almost the same instant a heavy tread was heard descending the main stair leading to the hall. Andrew's cheeks paled and his hands shook.

"Oh, for heaven's sake! Give me back my watch. We're altogether ruined, that's the laird himself," he gasped in a panic.

"It cannot be returned until all the spells are completed," replied Elspeth, in a solemn and determined voice, reflecting none of his fear.

At the same instant her husband deliberately placed his right hand on the hilt of the dagger which he carried beneath the large coarse outer jacket that he wore flung loosely over his shoulders. The other men in his gang, eight in all, at once followed his example. A moment later the laird, with a furious expression on his face, burst into the hall.

"What is the meaning of this?" he demanded fiercely. "Andrew Smith, what are you about? Answer me, you rogue! Answer me, or you'll hang for this outrage."

"Oh, sir, sir!" groaned Andrew Smith, wringing his hands in agitation. "Mercy, sir, mercy, I beg you!"

"You rogue!" repeated the laird, grasping him by the neck and throwing him to the floor. "What do you mean by carousing with such a gang as this? Answer me, you dog!"

As he finished speaking he kicked the stunned figure lying on the floor.

"Oh, sir, have mercy, I beg you," repeated the wretched major domo. "It wasn't my fault, really. They'll admit it if they but speak the truth. There was nothing else I could do."

"Now then! Out of this house, you gang of thieves and plunderers," went on the furious laird, addressing Willie Faa and his men. "You were born to the gallows. Get out of this house at once!"

"Thieves, is it, you landed dolt?" exclaimed the Faa king, leaping to his feet and drawing himself up to his full height.

"What right does the worm have that burrows in the lands of Clennel to address me thus? Thieves, you say! Speak such words to your equals, but not to me. Your forebears came over with the Normans, invaded the country and seized the land. Mine invaded it also, but only laid a tax on the cattle, sheep and poultry. And who do you dare call thieves?"

"That's enough, you impertinent beggar," snapped the laird. "The King's authority is in my hands and you should know it well enough. I warn you now that if I find you or any of your men again on my ground you will hang from the nearest tree."

"Boast away, boast away," replied Willie. "You are safe enough here from me and mine and it's a poor cock that cannot crow on its own dunghill. Just wait until the day we meet on the open moor, with only two bits of steel between us and see who will boast then."

"Outside you! At once, this moment!" commanded the laird angrily, drawing his sword and waving it threateningly above Willie Faa's head.

"Proud, cold-hearted and unfeeling man!" cried Elspeth. "Would you turn fellow beings from beneath your roof on a night like this when the fox would not emerge from his earth and even the raven would shiver in his tree."

"Out with you too, you witch! Out!" cried the laird, still in a fury.

"Farewell, Clennel," replied the Faa king. "We will leave your roof and seek the shelter of the hillside. But you will rue the day! I mean what I say. You will rue it!"

"He will rue it!" screamed Elspeth with an eldritch yell which raised the back hairs on many present. "He will rue it!"

Her dark eyes flashed and another eldritch howl filled the hall.

"Not only he will rue it, but the babe unborn will rue it too!" she went on determinedly. "The curse of Elspeth Faa will fall on Clennel and his kin this night, until his hearth is desolate and his spirit howls within him like the tempest which howls outside this night. For your want of humanity

163

this night your head will turn grey long before age has touched you and sorrow will bear hard upon you."

"Get out! Get out, you wretches," cried the laird even more angrily. "Vent your threats on the wind for I regard them as little as it will. But for the future keep out of my way and off my land unless you want to find a hempen collar round your throats and the hereditary exaltation of your kind."

Willie Faa signed to his followers and without a further word they left the hall, but as he reached the doorway last of all he turned and significantly striking the hilt of his dagger cried, "Clennel, you will rue this night!"

From the outer darkness beyond the door the hoarse voice of Elspeth echoed his words, crying out: "Clennel, you will rue it!"

When the door had closed behind the gypsy gang the laird dragged Andrew Smith to his feet. The man was still in such a state of terror that he could barely speak and the other servants were not in a much better shape. They had seen their money and prized possessions, along with Andrew's watch, all of which were supposed to have been returned, vanish with Elspeth and her gang. It was some time before the laird could make any sense of the proceedings, even when he lowered his voice and spoke mildly to them. In the end he realised that they had all been victims of the Faa gang's cunning tactics and declared that he hoped it would be a lesson to them all.

His anger with the gang was entirely justified, for he had suffered the loss of sheep, poultry and cattle. In addition they had ravaged his deer and even plundered his standing crops of grain, which was hardest of all to spare. These, however, had been Willie Faa's normal depredations, for he considered it his duty to spare no landed proprietor from paying him his dues.

In the weeks and months that followed the scene in the great hall, the Laird of Clennel began to learn what the gypsies had meant by their threats. His cattle sickened and died in their stalls, or the best of them simply disappeared.

His favourite horses were found, maimed and wounded, bleeding in the fields. Despite the vigilance of his shepherds the number of sheep he lost increased enormously.

The laird had no doubt that the Faa gang were behind these depredations, but he also knew their matchless cunning, which made it almost impossible except by pure chance to catch them in the act or bring the crimes home to them. Finally he came to the fields one morning and found his favourite horse, which had carried him safely through foreign wars, lying bleeding on the ground, with the tendons of both hind legs severed.

This was more than he could stand and he sent at once for a sleuth hound with an outstanding nose for following a trail of which he had heard remarkable feats. It was brought to him and set on some footprints which had been observed. With thirty armed men the laird followed the hound as it slowly pursued the trail over many miles of desolate country. Over bog and moor and mountainside it sniffed the trail, howling at times as if the prey was just ahead. Finally it led the way to a gap in the wilderness between Keyheugh and Clovencrag. Here in the space between the two desolate crags were a score of wooden and skin hovels, which formed the primitive fastness of the Faas.

"Now for vengeance," cried Clennel, seeing several of his prize cattle grazing round the huts.

"Bring whins and heather," he ordered. "Pile it round these huts and burn this thieves' den to the ground. Let us put an end to them at last, for once and for all."

His orders were quickly executed and when he called for a horn to be sounded only two or three old men and very old women, along with half a dozen young children, crawled out of the huts. Despite their howls of desperation as they saw what was intended the laird turned a deaf ear to their entreaties. A light was struck and half a dozen torches applied to the huts. The whins and heather soon took fire and the flames blazed round the huts which within an hour were merely a heap of smouldering ashes.

165

The Laird of Clennel and his followers returned homewards, driving the stolen cattle before them and very pleased with their success. On the following day Willie Faa and the rest of his tribe returned to their home in the remote mountains and found it a heap of still smoking ruins. The old men and women of the tribe, their fathers, mothers and grandparents, were sitting among the ruins trying to warm their freezing limbs over the embers and the children were weeping from cold and hunger.

"Whose work is this?" demanded Willie, his eyes flashing angrily as he surveyed the scene of ruin.

"The Laird of Clennel! The Laird of Clennel!" was the instant reply from half a dozen voices.

"By this I swear," exclaimed the Faa king, drawing his dagger at once. "From this day forward his days are numbered on the fingers of one hand."

He turned away from the ruins, sheathing his dagger, and making as if to depart at once to put his threat into execution.

"Wait, you madman," cried Elspeth, following him. "Would you fling away real revenge for half a minute's satisfaction?"

"No, wife," he replied. "No more than I would sacrifice a free and full life for half an hour's hanging."

"Stop then," she replied. "Let our vengeance come slowly upon him, drop by drop, gradually eating his life away until his heart is dry and grief, shame and sorrow burn him up, as he has burned the home of Elspeth Faa and her kin. Were you just to kill him with a length of steel through his heart that would be that, but the way I would suggest is a finer, sweeter way to make him suffer for the rest of his life."

"What do you mean, woman?" demanded Willie. "If I thought you were trying to deprive me of my revenge I would sink this length of steel in you as willingly as I shall drive it through him."

"And you would be welcome to do so," she replied.

Then drawing him close to her, she whispered in his ear

for several minutes. He listened with increasing attention. After some moments he sheathed his dagger and embraced her warmly.

"Excellent, Elspeth," he cried. "You have it. You have it. It will be as you suggest."

For the next two years or so after the burning the Faas' township the Laird of Clennel heard no more of the Faas. They did not, as he had half expected, return his attack, nor did they continue their thefts from his cattle, sheep or poultry. He naturally rejoiced in having got rid of such a dangerous nest of robbers, but Willie Faa, intent on following his wife's advice, was biding his time and waiting until the proper moment to complete his revenge with the maximum effect and cruelty.

At this time the Laird of Clennel was some thirty years old. Two years previously he had married Eleanor de Vere, who was distinguished not only for her beauty but also for her accomplishments. They had a baby son, who was the delight of his mother's eye and his father's pride. His name was Henry and he was just about then approaching his third year.

It was a pleasant warm April day when Lady Clennel and her baby son went out for a walk in the delightful woods surrounding Clennel house. The child, as infants will, sometimes ran ahead of her and sometimes lingered behind. Suddenly, without any warning, a man leaped from a clump of bushes, and seizing up the tiny child in his arms, darted back into the wood. Lady Clennel screamed for help and Andrew Smith, following her in something of a daydream caught a glimpse of the stranger and recognised the tall ragged figure of Willie Faa.

Although Andrew was usually slow to react in emergencies, this was a moment when even he was inspired. Drawing his sword he rushed into the woods after the fleeing gypsy with his precious burden. Although not normally a hero, he excelled as a runner and it was not long before he began to catch up with the gypsy king. Even so, the chase went on for over an hour and darkness was beginning to fall before

167

Andrew, younger and unencumbered, began to close the gap between them.

Andrew was within some ten yards of him when the gypsy king reached a bank of the river Coquet where for many yards the torrent flowed through a chasm in the rock before it fell over a hundred feet in foaming torrents. Knowing his ground well, the gypsy king raced for the one suitable spot and leaped the riverbank to land on the far side with no more than inches to spare. There he turned and, drawing his knife, faced the panting Andrew with an evil smile.

Even in this extremity Andrew's new found courage did not desert him. He paced backwards and forwards along the bank looking for a suitable place to leap and attack the gypsy king. The other paced along with him, his dagger at the ready. Finally he pointed with his dagger to the flooded river which foamed between them and cried.

"See, fool! Eternity divides us. Leap if you must, but you leap to your death."

"For the child's sake, you wretch, I'll face that if I must," replied Andrew with his teeth clenched and drawing back to make the leap.

"Hold back, man!" panted the gypsy, his chest still heaving with his exertions. "If you try to cross I'll drop the heir of Clennel in the river and you will follow him a moment later."

"Oh, you monster," gasped Andrew, his resolution deserting him. "What can I do?"

"Go back where you came from," replied the gypsy. "If you follow me the child dies."

"Oh, you butcher! You murderer!" cried Andrew. "Have you no mercy?"

"Just as much as your master had," answered Willie Faa, "when he burned our township about the ears of the aged and sick and my helpless children. I have all the mercy of a ravening wolf, or a tiger lapping blood."

Andrew saw that any hope of rescuing the child was over and returned home leadenfooted and with a heavy heart to report the events to his master. In the following weeks and

168

months the Laird of Clennel and his friends and servants searched anxiously throughout the countryside for any word of the child, but all in vain. There was no trace of Willie Faa or any of his tribe in all the areas they searched. All sign of him seemed to have vanished.

It was a long time before the Laird of Clennel, or even more particularly his wife, began to recover from the shock and sorrow of this tragic event. Four years passed from the time when their son was kidnapped and by then a baby daughter was sitting on Lady Clennel's knee. When the child smiled at her and reached up to her she was often reminded of her missing son and burst into tears, but she would then generally be comforted by her maid Susan, who had become part of the household two years previously.

With her golden hair and ready smile Susan was much loved by everyone in the household, especially the newly arrived daughter and her mother. Her affectionate manner and quiet nature made her a natural person to guard the new baby, to whom she was clearly greatly attached. It was thus another great shock to the household when one day it was found that both Susan and the baby had totally disappeared.

A great hue and cry was raised, but though they searched high and low through all the nearby woods and dragged the rivers and burns, no traces of either the girl Susan or their missing baby daughter were found. Again the household was plunged into mourning and both the Laird of Clennel and his wife were once more grief-stricken at this second loss so soon after their first. During the ensuing years, although their grief became less poignant, they still suffered great sadness at not knowing their children's fate.

After some fifteen years, during which nothing had been heard, once again sheep began to be missed and poultry stolen from the hens roosts. There could be no surer proof that the Faas, or their like, were somewhere in the neigh-bourhood, hiding in the thick woods which covered much of the countryside. Partly in the desire for vengeance and also in the hope that he might even yet learn some news of his children's fate, the Laird of Clennel again had resort to sleuth hounds.

Arming his servants, and with the sleuth hounds set on the likely trails, he and his men spent two days searching the neighbouring ground. On the third day the hounds raised a scent and set off at speed on the trail. The Laird of Clennel and his men followed swiftly and soon came upon the fires of a gypsy encampment. The hounds were ahead of them, already hurling themselves at the throats of the gypsies. They were responding with their knives and already several hounds lay dead as Clennel and his men arrived.

As they appeared the gypsies started to retreat, leaving behind only a golden haired sallow skinned girl vainly defending herself on the ground from the attack of one of the hounds. Clennel paused, undecided as to whether to chase after the fleeing gang and leave the girl to defend herself with her bare hands against the attack of the snarling hound, which had already mauled her arms.

"Rue it now!" cried the gypsy leader, with an evil laugh as he turned to flee from Clennel's men.

Maddened by these words, Clennel had already run past the girl in pursuit of the gang when a woman amongst the retreating gypsies ran back to him.

"For heaven's sake, Laird Clennel," she cried, "and for your sake, save my bairn!"

He turned back in a moment and, seizing the hound by the throat, tore it from the bleeding girl, who sank back exhausted and terrified on the ground. Her face was beautiful and her golden hair seemed an odd contrast with her torn and ragged dress. Then in a moment the older gypsy woman was by her side.

"Oh, my bairn," she exclaimed. "What has this day brought? They have murdered you. This is rueing indeed and I rue it too!"

"Susan!" exclaimed Clennel, thunderstruck, after gazing keenly for a few seconds at her face.

"Yes, it's Susan," she replied bitterly. "Guilty Susan!"

170

"Oh, wretched woman," he cried. "Where is my child? Is this she?"

Looking down at the bleeding girl lying on the grass his voice failed him.

"Yes, yes," Susan replied bitterly. "There lies your daughter. Just look at her face."

He did indeed only need to look at her face for a moment or two to see lying bleeding on the grass before him the same dearly loved face as her mother. He flung himself down on the grass beside her and, raising her head, he kissed her cheek tenderly.

"My child, my child," he exclaimed. "I have destroyed you."

He bound up her lacerated arms and hands and held a flask of wine which he carried with him to her lips. Lifting her head tenderly again, he kissed her gently.

"My child, my own child," he exclaimed.

Andrew Smith, who was still with him and had accompanied him on the expedition as of right, bent over his shoulder and gazed earnestly into her face.

"Oh, it is her right enough," he exclaimed eagerly. "I'd recognise her in a thousand or even ten thousand. She's the very image of her mother."

Turning back to Susan, for whom he had felt more than a passing affection and for whom he had grieved almost as deeply as for the child, he looked at her sadly.

"Oh, Susan, woman, what a terrible hypocrite you've been and what a traitor to the family!" he declared.

Having placed his daughter on horseback before him and supporting her with his arm, the Laird of Clennel started the homeward journey at an easy pace. Once returned to the mansion house he had his daughter's wounds carefully dressed and the stain removed from her face. Then with her toilet complete and her gypsy rags replaced by a dress more suitable to her station in life he led her to his wife's room to be re-united with her mother.

Aware that too much joy could have as undesirable an effect as too intense grief he was wondering just how to introduce the subject to his wife gently without being too

171

abrupt. The result was that his face wore a somewhat worried expression as he entered the room.

"Eleanor," he began at length. "Be of good cheer!"

"Why so indeed, my dear?" she asked in gentle tones of surprise. "I was not aware that I was sadder than usual, but surely it ill-becomes anyone who has endured the sorrows that I have to appear very cheerful."

"That is true enough," he agreed. "Yes, it is very true indeed. But the fact is that our affliction may not be quite as bad as we thought. There may even be reason to hope that there may be some joy for us yet."

"What do you mean?" she demanded eagerly. "Is there news of our children? Yes, I see from your face that there is. Tell me at once what it is!"

"Yes, my dear Eleanor," he replied. "It is true. There is news at last of our daughter. She is alive and well. She is indeed here."

He turned and opened the door, ushering their daughter into her mother's arms. An affecting reunion followed for several hours as mother and daughter and father too tried to come to terms with the sudden change which so affected their lives. At the strong intercession of their daughter, Susan was pardoned, forgiven and promised safety from the Faas' revenge. She then soon returned to the affection of the family she had forsaken and betrayed.

Before this, however, she was cross-examined by the laird himself and told her story simply enough. She was indeed an orphan, brought up from a babe by the gypsies, and treated more or less as a slave by them. She had been forced to take service in many households to learn secrets to pass on to the gypsies to make it appear that their fortune telling was, as they pretended, a product of the supernatural.

She had been in London when Clennel burned down the gypsy township and learned later of Faas' intention to kill him in revenge. Then she was told to gain access to the laird's family as a servant and finally to steal their daughter and to pass her off as her own. Of their son, however, she knew nothing. His fate, she was sure, was known to Willie Faa and his wife Elspeth, who had since been cruelly ill-treated by him and thrown over for another woman.

"If you could find her and cross her palm with silver enough, it might be that she would tell you all," Susan suggested to the laird. "But I heard her laugh when your hounds were set on your daughter and those she went off with will have travelled hard and travelled far. I cannot say where you might find her now."

The laird's disappointment when he was sure that he had learned all he might concerning his son was naturally particularly strong, for he had begun to have high hopes of finding him. Nor was the joy he had experienced in finding his daughter unalloyed for long. It was barely a year before the Civil wars broke out with Charles I fighting against his Parliament and his son Charles II taking over the struggle from him on his death.

The laird was a staunch loyalist and fought bravely for the Royalists. He fought at Worcester in 1651 when the Royalist forces were finally routed by the Cromwellian troops. With Charles II he fled to the borders of Staffordshire, where he bade his King a loyal farewell. From there he set off for his home in Northumberland. Although he was well aware that for the part he had played his person was likely to be in danger, his desire to see his wife and daughter again overcame his caution.

He had not gone far, however, when he encountered two men in the dress of the Parliamentary army. One by his grey hairs was a veteran and the other a handsome youth. Although it was already becoming dark he recognised the latter as a young man he had that very day wounded in the streets of Worcester.

"Stand!" cried the old man, when they met and the younger drew his sword.

"If I stand, it shall not be because an old man and a boy command me to do so," replied Clennel, following their example and drawing his sword.

"Boy!" cried the youth. "Who are you calling boy? Do you

173

think just because you wounded me this morning that fortune will always be with you? Yield or fight!"

After an exchange of thrust and parries the lad struck a lucky blow and Clennel's sword was broken in half, leaving him at his mercy.

"Now yield," cried the youth. "The luck is mine now, whereas this morning it was yours."

"You seem a fair enough foe," explained Clennel. "I am loathe to yield, but I am now weaponless."

"Kill him at once!" growled the old man. "If he spilled your blood this morning there can be no harm in spilling his tonight, especially after giving him a fair fight."

"Father," replied the youth. "Would you have me kill him in cold blood?"

"Let him submit to having his hands and eyes bound then, or I will kill him," replied the old man.

The younger man obeyed his father's orders and Clennel was led on with his hands bound and eyes blindfolded. After wandering for a good many miles and having slept on bare ground for the night and travelled on again the following day, he was brought eventually to a weary halt. The bandage was removed from his eyes and he was told to prepare for his trial.

Looking around he saw that he was in a gypsy camp, and although not a man given to fear he felt a sickness at heart when he thought of his wife and daughter and realised he was in the hands of the Faa clan. The males of the tribe began to form a rough half-circle and in the midst of them he saw the tall grey-haired figure of Willie Faa, whom he now recognised as the older Parliamentary soldier, but the youth he was unable to see.

He was roughly dragged before the half-circle of men and Willie Faa cried out: "Do you all know the culprit?"

"Clennel of Northumberland, our enemy," they cried out together.

"Yes," agreed Willie. "It is Clennel. The burner of our township, who left the old, the infirm and the helpless infants to perish. Had we burned his house the punishment would have been death, so shall we do less to him than he would do to us?"

"No, no!" they cried with one accord.

"But," added Willie, "though he would have disgraced us with a gallows, as he has been a soldier I propose that he has the honour of a soldier's death and that Harry Faa is appointed to shoot him."

"Agreed, agreed!" was the cry.

"Let him die then with the setting sun," decreed Willie and again the half-circle assented with a cry of "Agreed!"

Such was the form of rough trial which Clennel was afforded before being again dragged away and placed in a heavily guarded tent. He had not been there for half an hour when Willie Faa himself entered and addressed him.

"Now, Clennel," he said, "have I not lived to see a turn-about with you? When you turned us out from under your roof into the snow drifts, I warned you would rue the day. You mocked the threat and afterwards cruelly burned down our homes and turned my old mother that was three years short of a hundred out so that she was forced to cower over the reeking ruins without a roof to shelter her. There were my youngest also, crying with hunger at their grandmother's side, for you had burned all the food as well as their homes. That night I vowed vengeance and would have executed it at once, but I was prevented and glad I am now that I was, for my vengeance has been great and is now all but complete."

He paused for a moment with an evil smile.

"With my own hand I stole your son from his mother's side and a fearful chase I had of it. Revenge lent me strength and speed. And when you had a daughter I forced a lassie that some of our folk had stolen as a babe to bring her back to us. You have got your daughter back but not before she cost you many wasted pieces of silver and many a tear. That was some satisfaction, but the best of all is to come. You will die tonight as the sun goes down and the young soldier whom you wounded in the streets of Worcester and

175

who last night made you his prisoner is none other than your own son and heir. Ha, now! Am I not revenged in full now?"

"My son!" gasped Clennel. "You monster! Kill me now yourself, but do not torture me."

"Ha, ha, ha!" laughed the savage old gypsy. "Man, you do not know the half of it. I heard that you had joined King Charles. But who am I, a king myself, to care for either your king or your Parliament? I decided then to wear the Parliamentary cloth in the hope of meeting you as an enemy and seeing your son strike you to the heart. I did not have that satisfaction, but I did see you wound him and draw his blood in Worcester and in the evening he gave you into my hands as a prisoner."

"You monstrous savage!" exclaimed Clennel. "Have you no feelings at all? Tell me truly, have I seen my son?"

"Patience, man!" replied the Faa with another evil smile. "It was the blood of your son you shed in Worcester yesterday. It was he who disarmed you and made you my prisoner. And, best of all, it is he who will shoot you this night at sunset. Now tell me, Clennel, do you not rue it?"

"You evil, twisted monster," replied Clennel. "If I have raised my sword against my own son, let that suffice for your revenge. Do not have him kill his own father!"

"Quiet, you poor fool," replied Willie Faa contemptuously. "I have waited twenty years for the full consummation of my revenge and do you think I will be denied it now because of a few whining words? Until sunset!"

He left the tent with a final triumphant laugh and Clennel was left in a state of miserable tension, as may be imagined. It was not long, however, before darkness began to creep on and the sun started to sink behind the hills. Clennel was bound and brought forth into the open where a gag was placed in his mouth to prevent him making himself known to his son. He was tied to an ash sapling and the Faa tribe gathered round to watch his execution. The women of the tribe began a sort of wailing yell or coronach and their king, stepping forth with a savage smile on his face, called out,

176

"Harry Faa. Stand forth and perform the duty your tribe has imposed on you."

The young man, reluctantly and with a slow step, came forward. He carried a musket in his hand and placed himself about twenty yards in front of the prisoner.

"Make ready!" cried Willie Faa, in a thunderous voice.

The youth, although his hands shook, levelled the musket at the prisoner, but at that moment a figure erupted like a banshee from a clump of whins near the prisoner's ash tree. Throwing herself before the bound man she cried out in a piercing voice:

"Hold still, Harry Clennel! Would you murder your own father? Do you not remember when you were stolen from your mother's side as you gathered wild flowers in the wood?"

It was Elspeth Faa, now years older but still a figure of considerable power.

The musket dropped from the hands of the executioner and a thousand memories that he had fancied mere dreams crossed his mind in the instant. He picked up the musket and rushed towards his father, but Elspeth was there before him and had severed the ropes that bound him with a dagger which she placed in his hand for his defence. Instead with extended arms he embraced his son.

Willie Faa shook with rage and disappointment and he was filled with an impulse to thrust a dagger into his wife, but he feared to do so. Although he had cast her off and had not seen her for years his influence in the tribe had waned and she was now more powerful than he.

"See, Willie!" she cried out to him. "Who rues their actions now? Farewell for good and all. The lad I brought up will find me shelter for my old age and may you roast in hell!"

Such was her influence in the tribe that Clennel and his son were suffered to walk free with her unmolested, despite the curses of Willie himself. The rest is better left to the imagination. Great was the joy at the homecoming of the missing son and father both back from the wars. The mother's and sister's happiness was very great indeed and continued for many months and years. Andrew Smith was encouraged to place a ring on Susan's finger and old Elspeth lived on to the age of ninety-seven years under the protection of the Clennels, father and son.

To get the full flavour of the countryside featured in this tale, as good a place to stay as anywhere is Rothbury, an attractive small Northumberland hill town twelve miles south-west of Alnwick from which it is easy to tour Upper Coquetdale. Nearby is the eccentric home of armaments millionaire Lord Armstrong, which is seen at its best when the rhododendrons are in full bloom. A journey through the countryside around the Yetholms, Town Yetholm and Kirk Yetholm and beside the Cheviots will also help the reader to understand how wild this countryside once was. Esther Faa, the last Queen of the Gypsies, was crowned in Kirk Yetholm in 1847, when several hundred gypsies were said to have attended. She died in 1883, claiming to be the last of her tribe.

A SNOWBALL IN JUNE AND
MIDSIDE MAGGIE'S BANNOCK

Although the period of this tale overlaps with the previous one, it relates to honest sheep farming in the Borders around Lauder. In the mid-seventeenth century the Earls of Lauderdale, and this one in particular, did not have a particularly savoury reputation. However it is clear that already the old Border reiving days had passed forever. A man could now hope to rear sheep and make an honest living without fear of losing half his flocks on a moonlit night. The Crowns were united and the thought of any invasion from England was now long past, but the religious and civil strife which rent the Kingdom could still result in men in all stations of life ending up in prison, or losing their lives if they supported the wrong side.

THERE IS a sheep farm in Lauderdale close on the boundary of Berwickshire named Tollishill. In common with many such hill farms it was divided into three, each occupied by different tenants. There was thus Upper Tollishill, Lower Tollishill and Midside. The land was owned by John, the second Earl and later Duke of Lauderdale, a man well known for his shrewdness and guile in the conduct of his affairs, both in public and private. His tenant in Midside at this time was a tall, strong and red-faced man of fifty known as Thomas Hardie. Although inclined towards the Covenanting principles, he knew well that his laird was against them so rather than joining the religious struggle he remained on the fence.

Although nearing fifty he had remained a bachelor, but in the way of these things he duly met his fate. He had been down in Morpeth selling sheep when he arrived at Westruther after a much better market than he had expected with a heavy purse and a light heart. He stopped for some refreshment at the inn there where on such occasions three or four times a year he was in the habit of joining his fellow sheep farmers for a cheerful evening.

He was sitting there before the fire with a measure of the inn's finest ale when a young girl of around eighteen years entered to have a chat with the landlady. He was as good as lost on the spot. Her voice he thought the most delightful thing he had heard and her face was entirely beautiful while her figure was one that any man might have admired. Above all, however, it was her bewitching smile which completed his downfall. From being a perennial bachelor he was suddenly like a young man in love. The prospect of returning to Tollishill, which only a few moments earlier he had been anticipating with pleasure, seemed suddenly to be dull and lacking interest.

"Who would yon bonnie lassie be?" he asked the landlady when she had finally departed.

"She is indeed a bonnie lassie," replied the landlady, eyeing him shrewdly. "And seeing you are a single man, Maister Hardie, I am not surprised at you asking. Her name is Margaret Lylestone and she is the only child of a sickly old widow who came to live nearby a year or so back when her husband died. She is a cheerful good lass, who looks after her mother well by milking their cow and selling the milk and cheese, but even so they can't do more than just get by. She's a fine lass for all that. There's many a man might travel far and fair worse, but surely she's over young for the likes of you?"

It may be assumed that Thomas Hardie went home with the landlady's candid comments ringing in his ears, but as

180

is usually the case with a man in love, her remarks merely went in at one ear and out at the other. He returned home that day feeling fully twenty years younger and with a spring in his step and a song in his heart. Yet when he finally got home there seemed to be something lacking which he had never felt the need of before.

A few days later he was in Kelso market when a fine good-looking milch cow was up for sale. He noted that it seemed well tended and a beast after his own heart. He enquired from the auctioneer who was selling such a fine cow and was told that it belonged to the Widow Lylestone.

"And why would she be selling it?" he enquired thoughtfully.

"I cannot rightly say, Maister Hardie," the man replied. "Except that it can only be sheer necessity. The old lady's very frail and ill and the doctor's in attendance on her, I know, which all costs money. I doubt if they'd sell their only cow and a good one at that unless they needed the money badly. They've little enough else to live on. It's a grand beast, mind."

When the cow came up for sale Thomas Hardie outbid the others present and although he paid a good price for it he was pleased enough with his purchase. He then left the market rather earlier than usual and directed his herdsman to take the beast to Westruther. He himself went in advance and as darkness was falling he approached the widow's small cottage.

Outside the door he walked up and down indecisively for some time trying to prepare an explanatory speech, but when he finally knocked at the door and it was opened by the bonny Margaret his memory failed him completely. He stood stammering and speechless for a minute or so until she asked him in. There in the cottage by a peat fire sat her mother, supported by pillows in an armchair. He took off his bonnet and awkwardly bowed and introduced himself.

"I must beg your pardon for the liberty I have taken in calling upon you, Mistress Lylestone." he began hesitantly,

181

addressing himself exclusively to the old lady. "But when I was in Kelso today I . . ."

For a moment or two words failed him then he plunged on determinedly.

"I learned you were selling your cow and I also heard you were not at all well . . ." He paused again and then continued. "And I thought it was a bad time of year for you to be without milk and what the cheese may bring in . . . And the upshot is that I bought the beast and ordered my man to bring her back here for you to use as you wish. I'd not want you to think of the cow as mine, for a bachelor farmer like me can better afford to spare the money than you can spare the cow and I might well have spent it more foolishly and had less satisfaction from it, for if you only feel I've spent it well I'm more than paid."

For a few moments the widow's eyes filled with tears and she was hard put to it for words.

"Maister Hardie," she said finally. "How is it in my power to thank you? What have I, an old widow, done to deserve such kindness from you? Oh, Margaret my dear, what kindness this is from a stranger!"

With that both the mother and daughter burst into tears, to Thomas's great embarrassment.

"Oh, don't cry, please!" he begged. "I would never have bought the cow and would rather have lost the price ten times over than caused you to weep."

"Oh, Maister Hardie," smiled the widow, through her tears, "these are tears of gratitude we weep and there are none more precious."

That evening the cow returned to the widow Lylestone's small-holding and the next day the farmer called to make sure all was well with it. As the weeks passed he became an almost daily visitor, always ensuring that the old lady was well cared for and had all that she needed. He did not speak of his love for her daughter but wooed her rather by his constant attention to her mother and numerous kindnesses to her.

The old lady lingered on for several months, but finally

182

her time grew near and she was well aware of it. When Thomas Hardie appeared one morning she took his hand in hers and thanked him warmly for all his kindnesses to her in her last months.

"There is but one thing troubles me now,"she went on. "When I am dead who will look after my poor Margaret?"

"Oh, ma'am," replied Thomas warmly. "If I may say it, she has no need to look far for a home, for I would willingly give her that and my heart too, for that has been hers since the first day I saw her and all I have shall be hers, I promise you."

Both mother and daughter had come to feel warmly towards the burly farmer for his many kindnesses to them and at his words the old widow's eyes brightened. She reached for her daughter's hand with a sigh.

"And now I know you will be well looked after when I am gone,"she said. "You will marry this good man, will you not?"

Thomas Hardie's heart stood still as he waited for his bonny Margaret's reply, but she had come to feel a reciprocal love for him over the months he had attended her mother and though she wept as she held her mother's hand she answered steadily enough. "Have I ever disobeyed you, mother?" And smiling at Thomas himself in the way he could never resist, she added, "I will willingly take such a good man as my husband and hope to be a good wife to him."

"Oh!" exclaimed the farmer. "My bonnie Margaret, you have made me the happiest man on earth this day."

In due course Margaret Lylestone became Mrs Hardie of Tollishill, but in the way of the Borders she was more widely known, and famed for her beauty, as Midside Maggie. The old widow lived long enough to see them married and for two years after their wedding there was no happier couple in the Borders. Then came one of those very hard winters which all wise men who keep beasts fear most. Snow fell early and covered the hills and despite the best they could do many beasts perished in the snow-covered cleughs and glens. In particular Thomas Hardie suffered very grievous losses, with hundreds of sheep dead. In a single night he passed from prosperity to the brink of bankruptcy.

Another severe winter followed and with the loss of more sheep Thomas Hardie was unable to scrape together the necessary rent to pay for his tenancy and rent day was fast approaching. Seeing the agony of spirit which gripped her husband and well knowing the reasons for it, Margaret put on her best hat and coat and after telling her husband she was going into Lauder made her way to Thirlestane Castle where the Earl of Lauderdale lived. Before him any tenant in arrears quailed in terror.

After a good deal of explanation she eventually found her way into the Earl's presence.

"And what is it you're wanting, my bonnie lassie?" asked the Earl, eyeing her up and down appreciatively.

"May it please your lordship," she began. "I am the wife of your tenant Thomas Hardie of Tollishill, who has been a good tenant of yours these twenty years, as your lordship must well know."

"You say he has been my tenant for twenty years," interrupted the Earl. "And you're telling me you're his wife! Why, to look at you, I doubt if you're past twenty yet yourself. Damn me if Thomas Hardie is not a man of taste. Are you sure you're not his daughter?"

"No, my Lord," she replied. "I am his first and only lawfully wedded wife and I would only say to you that he has paid his rent regularly and faithfully these past twenty years to you and your father before you, but the past two seasons we've been under heavy snow and the bad winters have fairly destroyed most of his flock of sheep and we are barely able to hold our heads up amongst our neighbours. To pay the rent this rent day is simply impossible as we haven't the money. Therefore I have come to beg you to give us time to recover ourselves so that we may pay your lordship and our other debtors in full in due course when we are able to do so."

"Now just listen to me, my good woman," replied the Earl. "If I was to listen to such stories as yours I would have every farmer's wife on my estates coming whining and whimpering to me until I was left with no money in my exchequer and everyone living rent free at my expense. But it isn't every day that I see such a bonnie lass looking so doleful come before me, so, for one kiss from your shapely lips, and you may take my compliments to your husband on his good taste, you may have a discharge for your half-year's rent, and see if your husband can get on his feet again."

"No, no, your lordship!" replied Margaret firmly. "I am the wife of Thomas Hardie, who has been a fine man to me, and it would not be right for a woman in my situation, especially a married woman, to be dallying with someone like your lordship. I came here today merely to beg you to deal kindly with my husband in his misfortune."

"So!" snorted the Earl, who recognised solid virtue when he saw it, even if he did not necessarily practise it himself. "I have heard of the blossom of Tollishill before and a bonnie flower you are to grace an old man's bower, but you are as modest as you are bonnie and I will grant your request on one condition. You have told me you have been snowed up for two years in succession. It is now Martinmas and if you can bring me a snowball in June, not only will I waive your back rent but you may remain rent free in Tollishill until next Martinmas. But see you either bring me a snowball in June, or the rent."

Margaret took him at his word and duly curtsied, thanking him, and made her exit. When she returned home she faithfully told her husband of her journey to Thirlestane Castle and its outcome. Thomas, wiser in the ways of the world, kissed her affectionately and called her his "bonnie, artless Maggie", adding that he had no more chance of finding a snowball in June than she had and that this was merely a good example of "a crafty Lauderdale bargain", for the Earl was famed far and wide for always getting the better end of any deal.

Once again the snows fell heavily and the flocks were buried under the drifts, but Thomas and his shepherds battled hard to preserve the remaining sheep for the

Spring. When the weather began to ease it looked as if for the first time in three years they had some chance of a successful lambing. While the snow still lay on the ground, however, Margaret set out to a deep narrow cleft beside the river Leader where the sun seldom shone and where there was a deep sheltered overhang. On the hill above she formed a large snowball which she rolled into the cleft and from there, with considerable effort, pushed it under the overhang, which she then covered with branches from nearby rowan trees. She plastered them with mud and earth so that no light or air could get near it. She then returned home, but said nothing to her husband of what she had done.

When June approached Thomas Hardie was still unable to raise the money to pay his rent. He began to face the fact that his remaining sheep as well as all his household belongings would soon be seized by the Sheriff's officers and he himself clapped in gaol for debt. He spent much of his time glooming over the future and Margaret did her best to cheer him up to no avail.

"We shall have a snowball in June, even if I have to climb to the top of the Cheviot hills for it," she said.

"Oh, my dear girl," the farmer replied shaking his head sadly, "there's been no snow on the Cheviot hills this past month and, besides, there's no point in putting any faith in the Earl's words which were only meant as a jest at our expense."

Soon afterwards came the third day of June and the ominous and dreaded summons to Thirlestane Castle with the message: "June has come."

"And we shall attend at Thirlestane Castle tomorrow," answered Margaret.

"Oh, my dear," protested Thomas sadly. "You must accept the facts. Tomorrow I'll be on my way to gaol for debt and all I really care about is that goodness knows what will become of you."

"Don't worry about prison until you're behind bars," replied Margaret lovingly. "We'll see what happens tomorrow when it comes and not before."

186

Poor Thomas was reduced to an admiring silence in the face of his wife's courage and faith. For all that, he spent a sleepless night and woke the following morning haggard and wan. Margaret, however, was much like her usual self.

"Now, Thomas," she said firmly, "if you're ready we'll away to Thirlestane Castle. It's always worse to expect or think about something nasty rather than face it."

"Margaret my dear," he answered wonderingly. "Why should I stick my head in the lion's den, when it will soon enough come looking for me?"

"Come with me!" she replied, and led him down to the side of the river Leader into the cleft where the sun never penetrated. She then removed the rowan branches, still thickly coated with earth. Underneath the large snow-ball still stood, scarcely any smaller than when she had rolled it into position. When Thomas saw it he both laughed and wept at the same instant and kissed his wife warmly.

"My dearest wife," he said. "My poor Margaret. What trouble you must have been to and you've beaten the seasons, my dear, but I fear it was but a jest on Lauderdale's part."

"What is a man worth if he is not as good as his word?" protested Margaret. "And him a nobleman at that!"

"Noblemen are but men underneath," replied Thomas. "And seldom any better than other ordinary folk at that. Believe me, my dear, if we turn up before him with a snowball we'll just be laughed at for our pains."

"It was he who suggested it," replied Margaret stubbornly. "It was his decision and we can be no worse off for seeing if he will abide by his word."

Digging into the massive lump of snow she broke off enough to form a good sized snowball and rolled it into a napkin which she placed in a straw bag. Then, accompanied by her husband, she turned resolutely towards Thirlestane Castle, although on the way Thomas stopped again and again to protest.

"Margaret, my dear one," he argued, "I'm ashamed to be

carrying on in this way. As sure as I'm standing here we're just going there to be laughed at by the laird and all who hear of it."

"I would rather be laughed at," she replied staunchly, "than be despised for breaking my word; and if the laird breaks his word who would not despise him?"

Although they had previously led an almost blissfully harmonious married life, their journey to Thirlestane Castle brought them nearer to bickering than they had ever been before, for Thomas felt sure they were just wasting their time. In the end, however, they reached the castle and were ushered into the Earl's presence.

"Ha!" cried the Earl, as they entered. "Bonnie Midside Maggie and her old husband! Well, what have you brought me? The rents of Tollishill or their equivalent?"

Thomas looked askance at his young wife for he saw nothing in the Earl's face to give him any hope and he thought the word equivalent was uttered with a distinct sneer.

"I bring you a snowball in June, my Lord," replied Margaret. "Agreeable to the terms of your bargain, and I am just sorry for our sake and for yours that we have not yet been able to bring the money instead of it."

As Margaret opened her bag and unrolled the napkin to reveal the large snowball the Earl laughed loud and long. Thomas Hardie was thinking to himself that it was just as he had expected when, to his surprise, the Earl called for his writing materials. Then he sat down and wrote a discharge for Thomas Hardie's rent not only to that date but also until Martinmas to come.

Thomas Hardie bowed low and tried to find words to thank him, but stammered and stuttered awkwardly.

"Don't thank me," said the Earl, cutting him short. "Thank the modesty and discretion of your bonnie wife."

Margaret was silent as they left Thirlestane Castle, but her heart was filled with gratitude for the kindness the Earl had shown her and her husband. The unexpected and indeed unwonted generosity of the Earl enabled Thomas Hardie to overcome his losses and soon he was prospering again and was as well off as any farmer in the Lauderdale hills. In the meantime, however, by one of those quirks of Fate, the Earl himself had encountered misfortune, for this was the time of the Civil War and it was well known that he supported the King. That very same year, when the Commonwealth came to power under Cromwell, he was made prisoner and taken down to London to be tried and, since he neither could nor would deny his loyalties, imprisoned in the Tower. There he languished for nine long years, without the prospect of release and living without any of the comforts to which his lands and position might have entitled him to expect in more normal times.

Meanwhile the tenants who lived on his estates paid no rent and behaved in most cases as if they would never again see their landlord. Only Midside Maggie grieved for the man whose unexpected generosity had brought not only prosperity but actual riches to her and her husband. Duly, as each rent day came, from the Martinmas to which the snowball had been his discharge, Thomas regularly locked away the rent due down to the last farthing, to be delivered to his laird when he was able again to claim it. With heart still full of gratitude to their benefactor Margaret was always trying to find some way in which they could get the money to the Earl so that he might be able to use it to escape.

"Thomas," she declared finally, "there's ten years of rent due from us and here we are with the money locked away. Now it's no use to us, since it isn't ours in the first place, but it might be of some use to him, if he had it. For with a good-sized bribe to his gaolers it might aid him to escape and the rest could keep him alive while he's overseas. Just remember his kindness to us and think how there's no sin as mean as ingratitude."

"Aye, that's as maybe," agreed Thomas. "But just how are we to get the money to him, for if we were just to send it there's nothing more sure than that it would never reach him? As a prisoner he'd never be allowed to lay his hands on it."

189

"Well, we'll just have to take it to him ourselves," answered Margaret firmly.

"Take it ourselves?" exclaimed, Thomas, amazed at the suggestion. "All the way to London! It's out of the question, my dear. We would be robbed of every penny before we'd gone half-way; or, come to that, even if we got it there how could we possibly manage to get it to him, or even be allowed to see him?"

"Leave all that to me," replied his wife determinedly. "Only say that you will go and all that will be satisfactorily dealt with, I promise you. There's nothing to stop us but your agreement. Meanwhile the debt we owe the laird hangs heavy on my heart."

As might have been expected Thomas at last agreed to his wife's pleas and agreed to make the journey to London with a view to paying the rent owed, although he still could not see how they could possibly succeed in the venture. However Margaret soon revealed her plans and supplied the answers to his queries.

First she made him count out the gold coins which made up the amount owed. Then she took a quantity of barley-meal and made up a good sized bannock or loaf. When she had kneaded it and rolled it out she took half the gold pieces and pressed them into it, and then she kneaded it and rolled it out again and added in the rest of the gold coins. She then pressed it into a thick bannock, placed it in the oven and let it bake.

Thomas meanwhile watched the proceedings and marvelled at the ingenuity of his wife.

"Well, Margaret," he exclaimed, "I would never have thought of that in a thousand years. My dear, you are a wonder. You never cease to surprise me."

"Oh, away with you," she replied. "I'm sure you could have thought of just as good a plan. But mind, I'm sure there's not a thief between here and London likely to want to steal a barley loaf."

"In truth, I'm sure of that," agreed Thomas. "But surely there was never a loaf baked like the bannock of Tollishill!"

Three days later an old man and a young lad were to be seen crossing the border into England. They alternately carried a pack on their shoulders which contained some clothing and a large bannock. Both were dressed as shepherds with the familiar check plaids and Lowland bonnets, but the beauty of the boy's face attracted quite a few admiring glances, for the pair, of course, were Thomas Hardie and his Midside Maggie on their lengthy journey south.

Three weeks from leaving Tollishill, after an adventurous journey, they were not long past the town of Stevenage and almost within reach of London, when they encountered a military-looking gentleman, who was struck by the travel-stained but comely appearance of the youth and accosted the pair.

"Good morning, strangers," he remarked. "By your looks you will have travelled far. Is the lad your son, old man?"

"He is indeed," answered Thomas.

"And where are you from?" went on the stranger.

"First, just tell me who you are that are so inquisitive?" countered Thomas, a trifle testily.

"My name is George Monk," he answered mildly. "Some call me Honest George. I have the honour to be a general in the Parliamentary Army."

At this Thomas bowed and raised his hand to his bonnet in salute, but Margaret was not one to miss such an opportunity.

"If you are indeed the gallant general of whom we have heard you're not likely to take offence at anything a young country lad may say," she said. "We are tenants of the Earl of Lauderdale, who is now a prisoner and though we may not think as he thinks we have always found him a good and fair landlord and it can't do anyone any good to be locked up as he has been for over nine years now. So, even if our own business which has brought us to London were to fail, I will not regret the journey since it has given us the opportunity of seeing your Excellency and soliciting your interest, which must be powerful indeed, on behalf of our laird, that

191

you might release him from prison and, if he may not remain in this country, at least gain permission for him to go abroad."

"You plead most earnestly and fairly for your laird, my boy," replied the general, evidently much struck by her approach. "Though I do not think he is a man to be trusted it is true that he has been in prison long enough. Since you have brought his case to mind I will see what may be done for him."

He continued the conversation a little longer, asking further questions about their journey and their intentions, to some of which the replies he got were true enough and to others less truthful. However Thomas and Margaret went on their way very pleased at the encounter and hoping for the best from it.

Once in London Margaret dressed herself as a simple Scottish peasant lass with a basket on her arm containing a few ballads and the bannock of Tollishill. Acting the part of a wandering minstrel and affecting a silly air she went to Tower Hill, with Thomas following her at a distance to see that all went well. At the gate of the Tower she sang a ballad and attracted the attention of the officer of the guard there.

"What do you want, lassie?" he asked.

"Your alms, sir," she replied. "And to sing a good Scots ballad to the Earl of Lauderdale."

The officer and the guard laughed. They let her through the gate and pointed out the room where Lauderdale was imprisoned. Standing outside the window she raised her voice and sang *Leader Haughs*. The familiar haunting song of his native land drew the Earl to his window and he at once recognised the lovely face of Midside Maggie. He asked permission for her to be admitted to his room and the request was granted.

"Bless your sweet face," exclaimed the Earl as she was admitted into his cell. "And so you have not forgotten the snowball in June!"

He took her hand to raise it to his lips, but she withdrew it promptly.

"No, no, my good Lord, my fingers were not made for that purpose. Thomas Hardie is here," she said forthrightly, placing her hand on her heart. "Although just precisely now standing outside the Tower."

The Earl was naturally surprised and confused.

"Well, tell me, why you have come and why seek me out?" he asked.

"I brought you a snowball before, for your rent," she replied. "I bring you a bannock now."

And taking the bannock from her basket she placed it on the table in front of him.

"Woman," he replied, "are you really as crazed as I thought you pretended to be outside my window, or what?"

"The proof of the bannock," replied Margaret, "will be in the breaking of it."

"Then, my good woman, it may not be so easily proved," replied the Earl, taking the bannock and after a good deal of difficulty breaking it over his knee. When he saw the gold coins baked into it, however, for perhaps the first and only time in his life the Earl gave way to emotion and burst into tears.

"Well, every bannock has its worth, but the bannock of Tollishill beats them all," he exclaimed, recovering himself. "But I am afraid it's useless to me while I am still captive in this wretched prison."

"You have been a prisoner a long time," replied Margaret. "But it may not be hopeless, for not three days ago we met General Monk and, if what he said is true, before another week has passed you may be free to go abroad, where the bannock of Tollishill may be of use to you."

Lauderdale's amazement increased as he heard her words.

"Monk will certainly keep his word, if he gave it," he replied. "But tell me how this came about."

She explained the circumstances of their meeting and the general's words. As he listened a look of hope spread over Lauderdale's face. As he held her hand in farewell he made a final vow.

"Never will you rue the baking of that bannock, if old times ever return again," he declared.

Margaret then left his presence and returned to her husband, who was leaning on the railings overlooking the moat, anxiously awaiting her return. After a few more days resting in London and seeing the sights, they set out on their return journey to Tollishill. Meanwhile General Monk had remembered his promise and the Earl of Lauderdale was freed and allowed to go abroad, where, as Margaret had expected, he found the bannock of Tollishill extremely useful.

Several more years passed, during which Thomas Hardie continued to prosper and two boys were born to Margaret as his heirs. Then the Commonwealth ended and the King was recalled, bringing with him as one of his favourites the Earl of Lauderdale. On his return to Scotland as one of the most powerful men in the land, whatever else he may have forgotten, he recalled the bannock of Tollishill.

Attended by fifty men and in almost royal state he rode up to the house of Thomas Hardie and Midside Maggie. When they came out with their two sons beside them to meet him, he dismounted from his fine charger and produced a costly silver girdle of fine workmanship. This he fastened round her still shapely waist, and then gave her a deep bow.

"Wear this," he said. "For now it is my turn to be grateful and so for your husband's lifetime and your lifetime and for the lifetime of the generation I see beside you, you shall remain rent-free on the lands you now farm in return for the bannock of Tollishill."

Thomas and Margaret were too overcome to express their thanks and before they could try to put their feelings into words the Earl had re-mounted. With a wave of his hand to the family group standing in front of their farmhouse, he rode off towards Thirlestane Castle, while his followers all doffed their bonnets and shouted together.

"Long live Midside Maggie. Queen of Tollishill."

194

Thirlestane Castle just south of Lauder is well worth a visit. Lauder is a pleasing small town with several good hotels and makes a good centre for exploring the Lauderdale countryside and as far south as the Eildons and the Scott country, or east to Kelso and Greenlaw, or west over the hills to Earlston and Galashiels, or north over Soutra to Edinburgh and the Lothians. Lauderdale itself is a rolling, hilly countryside where sheep are still to be seen everywhere. Tollishill farm lies in the Lammermuir hills above Carfraemill.

DEATH AT THE WHITSOME FAIR

This tale overlaps with the period of the previous two tales, but continues into the latter part of the seventeenth century. Although still prior to the Union of the Parliaments, the borders on both sides had now settled down in the main to peaceful farming. Some of the old riotous spirit could be roused at fairs and similar meeting places, but apart from such occasions the countryside was mainly at peace. There were still some who indulged in smuggling over the border, but this was becoming less profitable as the years passed. There were, however, still reminders of the old reiving days and the divisions caused by the Civil Wars and by religious bigotry had also left their legacy here and there. In this final tale, which covers the area from the Merse deep into Northumberland, the effect of these legacies is seen.

WHEN border reiving became outlawed and its place was taken by law abiding exchange of cattle and sheep for cash, the reivers themselves were forced to become buyers or sellers at annual fairs held on both sides of the border. Such fairs as those of St Boswells, Chirnside, Swinton and of many other towns and villages are still continued. Others, for one reason or another, fell into disuse or have been deliberately discontinued. One such was an annual fair held at Whitsome, or White's Home, a small village and agricultural parish in the Merse bounded by the parishes of Swinton, Ladykirk, Edrom and Hutton.

Although the old practice of cattle reiving had been suppressed the law was unable to suppress the old rivalries and the old border spirit which had produced feuds in the past, many of which are not forgotten even today. As a result the meetings of old rivals at such annual events often led to riot and blood-letting and it was as a result of one such scene that the Whitsome Fair was discontinued.

The reasons for the feuds which so often caused the peace to be broken usually had their roots deep in the past. They mostly stemmed from the days when border reiving was a way of life, or from old border rivalries resulting from wars or battles long past. One such tangled tale was the cause of the Whitsome tragedy, which led to the ending of the Whitsome Fair.

One of the original participants in the feud which formed the background of this Borders tale was a daring young Northumberland border reiver named John Moor. He was courting a lass named Barbara, the daughter of one of the minor lairds of the border country, who in his day had been a particularly well known reiver himself, but who had been compelled to accept the authority of the Wardens after the two nations came under the authority of one King.

It was around Martinmas when the leaves were becoming few and blighted on the trees in the true autumn style. Barbara's father had consented to their marriage, but had made a slighting mention of the fact that young John Moor had but an ill-plenished house to take his wife home to, with neither meal in the chest, cattle in the sheds, nor oxen in the courtyard. Moor restrained himself from pointing out that a similar state of affairs existed in Barbara's father's own household, but instead took the usual course of doing his best to propose the action most likely to please the older man.

"Well, sir," he replied, "I cannot deny that what you say is true enough, but I am fleet of foot, I have a ready hand, a good sword arm and a stout heart. Furthermore I know where there are threescore fine cattle well worth the reiving."

"Well, well. Now you sound like a lad of sense and mettle," replied the old man approvingly. "And on the night you bring them home the plumpest and fattest shall be roasted for the marriage feast of you and Barbara."

Then up rose Barbara's brother Duncan, as likeable a young man as any between Tweed and Tyne.

"When you go to drive home that herd I will go with you, John," cried Duncan. "For the sake of tangling with that boaster Cunningham of Simprin? I will wager my sword against a tailor's needle that's whom you have in mind."

"It is he, Duncan," replied John Moor. "Though I know he keeps his cattle well guarded and blood will flow and weapons be broken before we possess them. But give me your hand, for we two will be a match for him and all his men. What you take will be your own and what I take your sister's, and your father will not complain about my ill-plenished house thereafter."

"Well spoken, my lads," cried the old man, who had seen many such an expedition in his younger days. "I am glad to see the spirits of the younger generation are not weakening although since King James went to be King in London as well as Edinburgh our laws have only been fit for old women and everything is done to make an act of manhood a crime."

"Do not go upon this mission!" Barbara implored them. "For there is blood on both your brows and death upon your path!"

"Nonsense, lass," cried her father angrily. "Are you at your fortune-telling again? What blood do you see on their brows more than I do or what death do you see in their path? All your mother's Highland kinsfolk were never able to prevent me doing what I wished for all their second-sight, and my daughter shall not either."

"Call it what you will," she replied. "But I see it as plain as I see the grey hairs on your head that death and lamentation are gathering round my father's hearth and are hovering and screaming over it like vultures round a desolate place in the desert where a man lies dying."

Her words made the flesh creep on John's bones and the foray was delayed until after their marriage, by which time she had almost persuaded John to give up the idea altogether. Then Duncan started taunting him, suggesting that he was no better than Samson lying with his head in Delilah's lap and that he had not only given his sister his heart to keep but his courage as well. Naturally this was more than John could stand and he reacted just as his brother-in-law had expected.

"Well, that does it!" he exclaimed. "We'll go tonight. The Tweed will be fordable at Norham. I will have my garron and weapons ready at eleven and get two friends I can trust to accompany us. You do the same and we'll see who needs courage in the morning!"

They shook hands on this as a bargain and at once began making preparations for the raid. On the appointed hour Duncan rode up to John's door with two of his father's men and John was waiting for him with two friends of his. Barbara bitterly and often repeated her warnings and they made John's heart beat uncomfortably.

"My husband – my brother!" she cried. "Listen to me and give up this mad excursion on which you are going. The bloodhound is sniffing the air and gnashing its teeth and the hooded crow is flapping its wings ready for a feast. The owl has its eyes fixed on Simprin. Be wise, be warned – or the sun will set on unburied bones. Again I say to you: be warned, do not go, or old men will tear their grey hairs and wives will mourn; and only those that live by the gibbet rejoice with the bloodhound and the birds of prey."

Her words made them feel uncomfortable, but they had all been on similar outings before this expedition and in the presence of the four men they had with them they could scarcely back down and change their minds. They were fearless and experienced hands at reiving, but the new and strongly enforced laws in the borders had severely restricted their opportunities and they were eager to get at the fleshpots, whatever the cost.

It was a fine, moonlit night and they went by way of Twizel to Norham where they crossed the Tweed to Ladykirk, where at midnight they passed the old churchyard. Both husband and brother, though they did not like to admit it, were very troubled in their minds by Barbara's prophecies and they scarcely exchanged a word as they went on their way.

Just around one o'clock, when the moon was beginning to edge down on the Lammermuirs, they arrived at the enclosure where Cunningham had some sixty head of cattle penned. The six of them had little difficulty in breaking down the gate that opened into the enclosure in which they were penned. Just as they were starting to drive them out, however, a figure stood up on a watchtower overlooking the cattlefold and started sounding a ratchet, making an appalling noise. This set the cattle lowing and the sounds could have been heard for miles.

It at once struck John that the best and wisest course was to put their spurs to their horses and be off as fast as they could back to Tweedside, for he knew that it would be hopeless even to secure a single cow when they would soon be surrounded by sixty or a hundred men. Before he even had time to move or speak Duncan's pistol flashed and with the sound of the shot the sentry sounding the alarm fell headlong amongst the cattle beneath him.

"You made a mistake in shooting that lad," cried John. "You have raised the whole countryside and Cunningham and his men will be on our heels directly."

They began to drive out the cattle and turn their heads towards the Tweed, but scarcely were they out of the enclosure when they heard the baying of hounds and the shouts of Cunningham's men.

Looking back and seeing that already around thirty men were behind them, catching up fast, and knowing the number would soon be doubled, John cried to Duncan, "Brother, let us spur our horses and leave the cattle to cover our retreat. It is no disgrace for six men to run before sixty."

"Be it so," replied Duncan.

However it was already too late. The cattle, scared by the shouts of the pursuers, tossed their heads in the air and ran wildly to and fro. The horses in their turn were scared to pass through them and they were so hemmed in by thick woods there was no riding round them.

Cunningham's men surrounded them with a wild shouting and cries for revenge. John and Duncan and their men sat shoulder to shoulder and fought them hand to hand. Soon two of the Cunninghams were rolling on the ground, but the position of the raiders was hopeless. Duncan himself was one of the first to fall. John was contending fiercely with Cunningham and hurled him from his saddle with a fierce effort, but as he rose to his feet his opponent thrust his sword through John's horse and he in turn was thrown to the ground.

Two of the other four were also wounded and the remaining two, seeing Duncan and John on the ground, surrendered. However John had not lost his sword and, hurling himself at his foes like a wild beast, he cut his way to the woods, though not before he had been wounded three times. Once in the woods he ran at full speed without any sense of direction until he finally came to a standstill and fell to the ground exhausted from his efforts and from loss of blood.

For a while he lay half-conscious until he heard a sound which slowly penetrated his senses. At first he thought he was out hunting, then the sound of the hound's baying came closer and he realised that a sleuth hound was on his tracks. It came gradually closer and soon he could hear it snuffling close at hand. He just had time enough to strike at it with his sword as it attacked. The blow was a weak one, broken by the branches of the bush against which he lay. Then he felt its paws on his chest and he was engaged in a life and death struggle as it tried to tear out his throat. Fortunately a lucky blow with his sword passed through its body and gradually its struggles weakened as he held it off with his hands round its throat. Finally its struggles ceased and it fell back dead across his legs. He himself lay back exhausted by his efforts.

It was plain that the hound's owners had lost touch with it, for no-one came to follow it up. Before morning broke he rose and made his way across the Tweed at Kersfield. The sun rose just as he turned the corner of the hill which brought his house into view and there he saw Barbara, his wife, sitting by the door as cold and frozen as if she had waited there all night, as indeed she had. Her eyes were closed, her hands clasped and her lips were moving as if saying a prayer or repeating a charm.

When she saw her husband approaching the door she rose from her seat and cried out to him.

"John Moor! You cruel man! Disregarder of the warnings of her whose life is as the shadow of your life! Did I not say that the hound was howling and the raven flapping its wings for a feast? Yet you would not listen to me! And my brother – where is my brother? – the son of my mother, more headstrong and foolish even than you yourself? You dare not answer and you need not answer. He is dead! The horses of Cunningham have trampled on his body and he lies unburied."

John Moor was unable to find words to answer her and in fact was hardly able to speak. The pain and stiffness of his wounds was bad enough, but he was also completely exhausted. There was a sickness in his heart too, so that he felt he could willingly have lain down and died and even have welcomed death as a weary man welcomes sleep.

He was almost recovered from his wounds before they finally learned of his brother-in-law's fate, when three of the four that had gone with them were allowed by Cunningham to return home. The other had died of his wounds a few days after the affray. From their account the sentry was none other than Cunningham's only brother. He did not learn of his brother's death until the affair was over and he was found lying in the courtyard into which the cattle were being driven. Cunningham then offered a free pardon to all his prisoners, except the one who killed his brother, on condition that they betrayed him. On hearing that, Duncan stood up boldly.

"I did it," he cried. "My hand brought him down from the sentry-box like a crow from its roost."

"To the turret with him!" ordered Cunningham fiercely. "And throw him from the top into the yard below."

This savage command was willingly obeyed and Duncan was carried to the top of the tower, then hurled to the ground. There he lay with the cattle trampling him and the dogs licking his wounds until he died.

When the news of his death was brought to them Barbara heard it in silence, but from that day onwards she was never quite the same woman. Her anger was awful and she vowed the day would come when she had her revenge in full on Cunningham. John Moor himself often told the story of the day's events to his children, for they had four sons, two sets of twins, ten years apart. He would always end by vowing that he wished the old days were back when he could meet Cunningham in the field and show him that the hand that had unhorsed him then could do so again and gain revenge for the death of his brother-in-law.

The years passed. The two eldest twins were twenty-seven and the two youngest seventeen when the Civil War broke out. Walter Cunningham, with his three older sons, joined the Royalist army, but his fourth son was still only a babe a few months old, whose mother had died in bearing him. Naturally this last child was very dear to him, but he left him in the care of a good old retainer and set off to the war with his older sons.

When John Moor heard that his old enemy had joined the King's forces, that was enough for him to join the Parliamentary side with his sons, although as a true Borderer he cared little enough for either. Barbara protested bitterly at his decision.

"Why, John, must you sacrifice yourself and our bonnie lads in a war that's none of your wanting? If you go now you rush on swords that are sharpened for your destruction and you hasten to fatten the raven and the worm. The winds will

203

sing your dirge and the gloaming and the night fling a shroud over your uncoffined corpses. You go, but you will not return. You will see the sun rise, but you will not see it set and those are hard words for a wife and mother to have to say."

Despite inward misgivings John Moor and his sons were natural warriors and the chance of battle, no matter on which side, was too good to miss. Taking the route by way of Coldstream, Greenlaw and Soutra Hill to avoid General Leslie's army, which then occupied the eastern end of the Lammermuirs, they reached Dunbar at last, where they enrolled in Cromwell's army.

A few days after their arrival they joined a skirmishing party and in a wild glen not far from Spott they met up with another similar company that had been sent out by General Leslie. Their commander was Walter Cunningham and in the forefront were his three sons. It was with a look of ruthless delight that John Moor saw his old enemy opposing him.

"Yonder is the murderer of your uncle," he said to his sons. "There is Cunningham of Simprin with his three sons, well mounted and riding behind him. But before night their pretty hats and feathers will be trampled in the ground and it will be music to your mother's ears that her brother's death is avenged at last and by the hands of his own flesh and blood."

The two parties rode forward and faced each other. The Cunninghams and the Moors sat their horses face to face. The two fathers sat as if fixed in their saddles. They eyed each other with looks of hatred and ferocity, each recalling the days and the strife of years past.

Though neither side had more than fifty men the battle was fierce and furious and the struggle was long and desperate until on each side more than half their number lay dead or wounded on the ground. Amongst the dead were the four sons of John Moor and the three sons of Walter Cunningham. The old men themselves maintained a desperate combat with each other apart from the rest until finally, breathless and exhausted, both paused for a few moments, each holding his sword pointed at the other. For the moment they stared at each other's face and at the bodies of their dead sons on the ground. Grief on both sides resulted in redoubled rage and effort and they set to once again with their swords clashing loudly against each other.

After a long and fierce struggle both fell to the ground sorely wounded, but John Moor had received a death wound as he lay on the ground and knew he would never rise again.

"I am dying," he gasped, still holding his enemy in a death grasp. "My children too are dead. But remember there is one left to avenge our deaths and she will avenge us sevenfold."

When the news of the death of her husband and her sons was brought to Barbara Moor she sat transfixed. The messenger repeated his melancholy news twice and when he received no reply departed, marvelling at the silent sorrow of the widow.

"I knew it, man!" she said, after the messenger had departed. "I knew they would not return to me! I told them but they would not heed me. But I will live to be revenged for their deaths and my brother's death too. Their murderer shall not dandle a child upon his knee or kiss its cheek, while mine are all dead."

From that day she left the comfortable farm house in which she had lived and wandered the countryside seeking shelter where she might and living at best in a small mud-built and turf-roofed hovel, which afforded little protection in the winter months. There had always been a tinge of extravagance and an element of vehemence in her actions, quite out of the ordinary, but this now greatly increased. It was generally accepted that affliction had turned her brain for there was wildness in her words and in her manners which were not those of ordinary women.

Meanwhile, on his return sorely wounded from the war Walter Cunningham spent much time with his young infant, the flower of his old age and now the only son left to him. In the nature of things also the number of his flocks and of his herds steadily increased and he spent much of his time attending fairs around the borders to dispose of them and buy new stock.

Whitsome Fair was one of those he attended and when its time came near he sent on many of his sheep and cattle to be sold. He also attended it himself, taking his young son, then aged a little over three years, with him. It was approaching evening and Cunningham, engaged in a deal with a buyer, left his child in a tent while he concluded matters. On his return the child was missing and despite the father's frantic appeals no-one had seen him or could find any trace of him. For many days his sorrowing father searched for news or trace of him in vain. He returned to his home a heart-broken and sad old man, visibly aged in the few weeks he had been away. For several years thereafter he remained in lonely misery, hardly moving from his house.

It was on a dark and dismal winter's night some seven years after the disappearance of his son, when the hail rattled fiercely against the window panes and the wind howled wildly through the keyholes, that a high-pitched eldritch voice was heard singing a wild dirge, as if in accompaniment to the storm. The sound came from an open shed near to the house where the cattle had been given shelter.

The servants informed their master that a strange woman, who seemed disordered in the wits, had crept into the shed, where, owing to the fury of the storm she would doubtless perish before morning. They took a light and he accompanied them to the shed. There a wild and wretched being sat on the straw, her long grey hair waving loose and wildly in the wind. Her hands were clasped over her breast and she sang a wild and melancholy dirge in which one word only dominated: "Childless – childless – childless!" As they listened it waxed louder and was wildly sung as a prayer for vengeance. Tears gathered in Walter Cunningham's eyes as he listened and his body shook visibly.

"Take her into the house and give her food and shelter

for the night," he ordered. "If my poor boy yet lives he might be perishing with none to shelter him."

At his mention of his son she suddenly ceased her wild singing and started to her feet. Her eyes glared at him from her haggard features, while her long grey hair and ragged clothing blew about in the gale. She seemed more like some demon of the storm than an inhabitant of the earth.

"Ha, ha, ha!" she cried, with a hideous laugh, which made the hearers shudder. "Shelter – from you, the murderer of my brother, my husband, and my sons! You that have made me childless! Back to your kennel, dog, and if it will add another moment of torturing anxiety to your miserable soul be it known to you that your son still lives and you may see him but never know him – just know that he lives!"

"Where is he, woman? Where?" cried the wretched father.

She dashed a lantern from the hand of a servant who advanced closer and rushed from the shed into the open fields laughing more loudly than she had shrieked before.

"Where indeed? She, whom you have made childless leaves that to torture you for ever!"

The lamp which she had thrown aside set light to the straw and, although the grief-stricken father rushed after her into the darkness, the servants mostly stayed to put out the flames. In the ensuing confusion the woman was seen no more. Who the woman was he had no idea for Barbara Moor had not been seen in that part of the country previously and her words, as she had hoped, merely increased his anxiety and misery.

At this stage it is necessary to introduce Sandy Reed, a widower of around fifty with an only daughter named Ann, aged four years, whose house near the Reed Water in Northumberland was kept by a maiden aunt. He was as fine and typical an old Northumbrian farmer as could be found in the area.

When he had business in Morpeth market his journey home never occupied less than a fortnight, although the distance was less than thirty miles, for he had perforce to stop at every hostelry by the way for the sake of the company. At the same time he did not mind going half a dozen miles out of his way to include another such source of entertainment in his way.

He had been over at Morpeth market with sixscore hogs and fourscore ewes and he was, as he put it, "comfortable" when he left Morpeth. At this stage he had only had twenty measures of English gin, by which he meant Cheviot whisky, and as he pointed out later, several of those were public-house measures, only making about three or four good ones. Regarding himself therefore as completely sober he decided to go round by Elsdon to see what his friends there were doing. His horse, which knew the way round all the local inns as well as he did whether he was drunk or sober, knew where he wanted to go when he pulled the rein to the right.

"Away to Betty Bell's at Elsdon," he commanded, and the horse turned across the moor obediently, ending up as if he had been guiding it all the way, at the door of the Elsdon inn.

When he entered this second hostelry he found five of his friends sitting drinking. All welcomed him with cheery greetings.

"Ha, Sandy, lad!" they cried. "You're right welcome. We just wanted you to make up the half dozen. Have you been at Morpeth market?"

"Yes," replied he. "And I just thought I'd come round by Elsdon to have a cup with you."

"So be it!" they replied and they all sat down to steady drinking for the next three days, when, while they might have been ready to drink more, Betty Bell's cellars had run dry.

Sandy Reed's recollections after that were perhaps a little confused. He remembered getting back on to his horse, which had been feeding well in Betty Bell's stables in the meantime. By this time, however, it was evening and the stars were winking in the sky. As he himself put it, he was winking as badly as the stars, but turning his horse's head for home, he somehow stayed in the saddle for a while at least, although nodding off to sleep and swaying in the saddle.

How it happened thereafter he had no real idea. Perhaps something scared the horse and he slipped from the saddle. He remembered lying on the thick heather of the moor and feeling very sleepy. He also remembered lying half-awake and thinking he was cold and calling for his aunt to bring another blanket and admitting to himself that he was perhaps more than a little the worse for drink. Then he felt a small head on his chest and thought perhaps it was his daughter Ann. He felt the head and gave it a slight shake when there was a squall which wakened him in astonishment and brought him to his senses and scrambling to his feet.

He had been lying in the open moor, with his horse grazing beside him and a small raggedly wrapped infant was now lying in the heather at his feet yelling with the full power of its lungs. Although he immediately looked around him to see who had left it, there not a soul was to be seen. He tried speaking to the child, asking it what its name was and where it came from, but it merely cried louder than ever and it was plain it did not understand a word. Next he tried shouting at the top of his voice.

"Is there anyone around who has lost a bairn?" he bellowed, but not a soul appeared.

He half came to the conclusion that it must have been left by the fairies, although he had seen no one, but he had heard enough of their deeds. Although swaying a little as he stood and still somewhat muddled in his thinking, he realised that he could not leave the child out on the moor by itself for it was sure to die and he felt he would never sleep well in his bed again if he were simply to abandon it in that way. On the other hand if he took it home he knew that his neighbours would all laugh and think it was his own and his aunt would probably lecture him endlessly about it. Nevertheless he decided there was nothing else for it and, setting the child on the saddle in front of him, he took him home.

"What is this you've brought home, Sandy?" demanded his aunt as she came to the door to meet him.

"It's a bairn I found on the moor,"he explained.

"I trust you are not the father of it, Sandy?" she demanded.

"I'll give you my word, I'm not," he replied, "and I know neither the father nor mother. From the way I found it on the moor I doubt whether it had either one or the other."

His aunt was more easily satisfied than he had expected and by degrees he told the story of finding him to his neighbours, who also took it less boisterously than he had expected. Over the years no one came to claim the child and he reared him as his own along with his daughter Ann. As the boy grew tall and strong Sandy Reed was immensely proud of him as if he was indeed his own son. The boy, whom he had named Patrick Reed, also came to love Sandy's daughter Ann with whom he had grown up. It was Sandy Reed's dearest hope that they should marry when Patrick reached what he judged to be twenty-one.

One thing that worried the old Northumberland farmer a little was the appearance in their area of a half-mad old woman named Barbara Moor, wandering round the moors, who spoke occasionally to his children and seemed to put strange ideas into their heads, for Patrick especially was often disturbed after she had departed. On one occasion he confessed that she had told him she would read his hand. Then she had told him his name was not Patrick Reed, but another. Something about her appearance had conjured up confused memories of the past and the youngster was greatly worried by it, although Sandy Reed tried to laugh him out of it.

When Patrick was about eighteen and Sandy more than three score, the latter started growing turnips in the lower fields of his farm and decided to go to Whitsome Fair to buy some cattle. As he felt that he was now less capable of such long journeys as he had been in the past he decreed that Patrick should go with him. As his adopted son and prospective son-in-law, heir to his farm, he considered it right that he should have a hand in deciding what beasts they should buy.

On the evening before they left for the fair, Ann, who had been visiting a neighbouring farm, was intercepted on the moor about a mile from her home by the wild and witch-like figure of Barbara Moor. She held up a hand to halt her.

"Stand, maiden," she cried. "You love the young man your father calls Patrick Reed and he loves you, is it not so? If I who have his destiny in my hand can control it you shall be wed. But there must yet be more blood, for I am childless! We are not even yet!"

She struck her brow with a wild gesture and continued.

"Yes. You shall be wed. And you deserve happiness. But listen, maiden, well! For on my words depends your fate! When your father and his Patrick go to Whitsome Fair insist that you accompany them and then you will return here a wealthy and wedded wife. Swear that you will do as I say."

"Woman," replied Ann, shaking a little as she spoke, "I will not swear, but I give my word I will do as you say. I will go to Whitsome Fair with my father and Patrick."

"Go, go!" cried the old woman. "Lest the dark spirit take me and he whom you call Patrick shall die by his father's hand, or his father by his. But speak not of what I have said. Be silent till we meet again."

With these words the wild, old, witch-like figure turned and sped off at surprising speed across the moorland, disappearing in a matter of moments behind a fold in the hills. Some minutes later, when Ann returned thoughtfully to the house, it was to find her father and Patrick, her adopted brother and betrothed, making their preparations for their departure that evening. As she sat herself beside them, her pale expression caught Sandy's eye.

"Why so woebegone, daughter?" he asked. "Are you sad because Patrick is to leave you for a day or two to go to Whitsome Fair? I am sure you would not have been bothered had I been absent for as many months. However I don't blame you. I was as soft-hearted at your age. No doubt Patrick will be able to comfort you better than I."

"What is the matter, Ann dear?" asked Patrick, sensing that something more serious was worrying her.

"Ask father," she said hesitantly, "if I may accompany you to Whitsome Fair tomorrow."

"No, my dear," replied Patrick. "You would not enjoy it. It is a long, rough ride and there is rough enough company at the end of it. It would give you no pleasure, I promise you."

"I feel I must go," confessed Ann. "That wild old woman on the moor made me promise to do so."

"Old Barbara Moor!" exclaimed Patrick, frowning. "There is something about that woman which sticks at the back of my mind and seems to haunt me. Her face seems to have been part of my dreams from childhood yet I only saw her first two or three years back. She has a strange way with her. Yes, I think you should come."

He turned to Sandy Reed whom he regarded as his father and put the request to him.

"Let Ann come with us, father," he asked. "She requests it and I also wish it."

"Oh well," grumbled Sandy Reed. "If the pair of you have made up your minds I don't suppose there's anything I can say will make any difference to you. So, Ann my dear, if you wish to go you'd better go and get ready, for we'll have to leave here by twelve o'clock tonight at the latest. It's a long ride and a rugged one as you'll find out for yourself before you return here. Make sure you wrap up well now."

At midnight Sandy Reed, his daughter Ann, his adopted son Patrick and three or four farm servants all departed for Whitsome Fair mounted on light, but strong and active horses well used to long journeys over hard going. They reached Whitsome at noon the following day, having crossed the Tweed at Coldstream. There they looked over the cattle on sale.

Amongst the most prominent sellers was Cunningham of Simprin, with several hundred cattle up for sale. He now left almost all the transactions to a nephew who had accompanied him and whom he had named his heir, but he himself was also there, although now old and careworn. Having carefully looked over all of the beasts present Sandy

212

Reed decided that Cunningham's cattle were the ones he wanted. After a great deal of bargaining and the payment of a good round sum Sandy Reed eventually became the owner of Cunningham's cattle.

When the deal had been struck the buyer and seller and their respective followers retired together, the seller to treat his new customer with a bottle and the latter to spend the "luck-penny", which on such occasions he always said was inclined to "burn a hole in his pocket".

Both the old men were accustomed to drinking heavily, for Cunningham in his old age had taken refuge from his sorrows in the bottle. Sandy Reed watched with some vexation as he swallowed glass after glass with no apparent effect, for he had never met his superior at drinking, or much else. In due course the two old men began to forget their age and started boasting of their past deeds and, forgetting that each was past threescore years, they every now and then would start to profess what they could still do. Ann sat at Sandy's elbow gently and quietly restrained him.

However, Sandy was unable to resist boasting of the strength of his son Patrick and offered to match him against any man in Berwickshire, or for that matter the whole of Scotland. This was too much for old Cunningham and he offered to back his nephew against the son of his new found Northumbrian friend.

"It's a bargain," cried Sandy, rising to his feet in his excitement.

The two young men then began various trials of strength, but strong as Cunningham's nephew appeared, Patrick was always much stronger. Their countrymen supported them ardently on both sides but the supporters of Cunningham's nephew became angry as Patrick easily overcame his opponent. Knives were drawn and blood was spilt. Foremost in the fray, but unarmed was Sandy Reed, knocking down a man at every blow. At last he fell to a knife thrust and his dying words were: "Revenge me, Patrick. Look after Ann – all I have is yours."

When weapons were drawn Patrick drew his and dealt a

wound at every blow. As he saw Sandy Reed fall and heard his dying words he seized old Cunningham by the throat and was about to avenge his adopted father's death when a loud voice screamed in his ear.

"Stop! Stop! Do you wish to kill your true father? He it is you hold by the throat!"

It was the familiar screeching voice of Barbara Moor and the lad's hand fell to his side as if paralysed.

"What are you saying?" gasped Cunningham, barely able to breath even though the grip on his throat had been released. "Who is my son? How shall I know him?" he begged in agonised tones, for he too recognised the familiar figure of Barbara Moor.

"It is he who has just now nearly killed you," she replied, sinking to the ground, for she herself had received a fatal knife thrust while forcing her way through the brawl. "You will find a strawberry mark on his chest which you will remember. Now I die childless, while you are not. Farewell!"

She did not die immediately, but lived long enough to confess how she had stolen the child from the tent at the fair where his father had briefly left him, then gave him a sleeping draught, and how she came on Sandy Reed lying on the moor and left them together. The joy of old Cunningham was perhaps only matched by the chagrin of his nephew who had hoped to be his heir. Although Ann grieved greatly for her father she agreed to an early marriage with the man she knew as Patrick Reed, now known as Patrick Cunningham. As Barbara Moor had foretold, she returned to the farm in Northumberland a wealthy wedded woman. The fountain where Sandy Reed fell is still known as Reed's Well, but the Whitsome Fair has never been held since that day.

Whitsome is a small hamlet about six miles north-west of Berwick. Reed's Well still exists.

Berwick is an obvious and excellent choice for exploring the Merse as well as for touring the Cheviot area and north Northumberland. An old, walled town at the mouth of the Tweed, it is anyway a delightful place to visit.

Elsdon, where Sandy Reed stopped at the inn, is a very attractive Northumbrian village high up above Rothbury. When the fourteenth century church was being restored over 1,000 skulls were discovered, supposedly those of English soldiers killed at the battle of Otterburn.